Braids & M

MW00805710

Written by: Andrea Jeffery

Editor: Margaret-Rose Best

Artist: Shelagh McCallum

Photographer: Roy White

Hair Stylist: Andrea Jeffery

Models: Judy Burr
Jan Campbell
Jean Cichon
Andréa Parsons
Jennifer Pettigrew
Lindsay Stubbs
Joyce Wills
Lauren Woolstencroft

ISBN: 0-9693543-1-2

Publisher: Zöpfe Publishing Incorporated
Printed in Canada

Table of Contents

Table of Contents *(cont'd)*

Dedication

This book is affectionately dedicated to my husband, Brian, and to my children, Andréa and Sean. I thank them for contributing their ideas to the book cover and contents and for their patience as the book took shape.

Acknowledgements

Thank you to Margaret-Rose Best (Beauty Culture Teacher for the Calgary Catholic School Board) for the editing of this book. Margaret-Rose is an exceptionally busy person and made special time to edit this book. I appreciate her dedication to the book 100%. She was an asset to the book because of her knowledge as an English teacher as well as a Beauty Culture Teacher, plus her love for long hair.

Thank you to Shelagh McCallum, professional artist of the book, for the many hours she spent on the drawings in the book. Your work is fantastic Shelagh!

Roy White, professional photographer, did a lovely job taking pictures of the models with their completed hair styles. You did it again Roy, for the styles look great!

I wish to thank the eight models for coming to practice runs for all the styles I wanted in the book. They kept their hair long so I was able to do each style without any problems and I truly appreciate their dedication and patience. Thank you ladies, for you were terrific!

About the Author

Being the co-author of the book, "Braids & Styles For Long Hair," has kept my interest in creating new syles for long hair. I'm an instructor of hair braiding at Mount Royal College in Calgary, Alberta, Canada. I have been instructing classes there for six years.

Through my hair braiding classes I acquire many imaginative ideas for long hair. Several of my ideas derive from everyday fashion items: shoelaces, ribbon, rope, scarves, barrettes, and scrinkles.

I'm very aware, while in public places, of the hair accessories that children, teenagers, and adults wear in their hair and how they use them to give a special affect to a particular hair style.

After seeing many girls and women wear barrettes and covered elastics (scrinkles) on their ponytails, I decided it was time these people have a helping hand with some suggestions for using these accessories. The result of my many ideas led to writing the book, "Braids & More."

The terminology I use for braiding is very different, but it works well for people because of the step by step instructions, with diagrams to show visible patterns. My method does not mean it's the only method, but only that it's a method or way of explaining various styles which works well for the majority of individuals. If you are not familiar with the terms used in the instructions of the book, then use the glossary.

History of Braids

Braids are mentioned in history as far back as the Ancient Egyptians. Braids on Egyptian wigs are found as early as 2900 B.C.. In 1025 B.C. Princess Na-ny, daughter of King Pinedjem, wore a wig with a long narrow braid of human hair. Roman women are also mentioned wearing braids as early as 50 B.C.

Braiding makes its' most significant appearance during the 12th Century in France. First, with braids wound around the head and later with long and extended braids. Braids were often extended artificially to obtain exotic lengths. The English, Germans and Italians are mentioned wearing braids as early as the 14th Century A.D.

The Renaissance. It began in Italy about 1300 and spread throughout Europe during the 1400's and 1500's. Some people had long braids that fell to their knees.

Periodicals start to recognize braiding in the early 1700's.

Hairstyles in the 1700's were decorated with flowers, jewels, or other ornaments.

In 1754 the Connoisseur reported that braiding was on an uprise. In the 1840's rolls came in and were wore various ways on the head. Instructions on braiding appear in 1853 with the release of Godey's Lady's Book. In 1870 in Paris, a popular magazine called A Lady's Friend suggested braiding hair the night before to get a crimped look.

Then Africa came into the hair braiding picture. In North Africa (the Mahgreb, inhabited by Tunisians, Algerians, and Moroceans) girls wore their hair partly shaved and partly braided from birth until they were twelve years old. In adolescence the hair was allowed to grow evenly all over the head and was braided simply.

West Africa-the Sahel. Girls had their hair cornrowed or simply braided until they married.

In tropical West Africa two traditional techniques for styling hair have survived to the present day-braiding (cornrowing) and hair threading (process of wrapping the hair with thread).

In Central Africa the Bambala women had two methods of dressing their hair: one involved shaving the front part of the head and blackening it with soot, while the hair on the back of the head was plaited into tresses and painted with a mixture of soot and palm oil; the other method was to arrange the hair in longitudinal ridges and dye it with the aid of red ferruginous clay.

Mangbettu people made hairpins from copper, wood, ivory or bone.

In East Africa the Masai warrior grew his hair very long and had it styled by a fellow warrior (moran). The moran smeared the hair with fat, red ochre and clay and twisted the hair into as many as four hundred strands. The strands were grouped into a style, using sticks and sheep skin for accessories.

In Southern Africa the people adopted a very wide range of hairstyles-wider, perhaps, than that of any other part of the continent. The hair twisting method was very popular in that area.

In Malagasy Republic the Betsileo women relied on their exquisite hair styles to attract the attention of men. They arranged their hair in countless single braids, designed to look like flat curls all over their head.

Over the past fifty years Western culture has infiltrated Africa.

Those who traveled to Europe and the United States brought home with them ideas and fashions. While the tribal rulers did their best to uphold tradition, the Western-educated few were regarded as trend-setting members of society, apostles of a new order.

Change was in motion: old customs started to give way to new alternatives.

Developments in Africa coincided with the rise of the civil rights movement in the United States. The afro was for some time symbolic of Black militancy, it soon became generally fashionable. After the afro came the cornrowing craze.

There were two methods of cornrowing. One method was to braid with an overhand motion, sometimes known as "right-side" cornrowing; the other was to braid with an underhand motion, known as "wrong-side" cornrowing.

Blacks had never dared to display it publicly. Braiding and cornrowing were considered acceptable for children but unbecoming on adults. The actress Cicely Tyson helped to change this attitude by wearing her hair cornrowed on television. She startled the nation, but the style captured the imagination of culture-conscious Blacks, who began to try out the technique for themselves. Cornrowing spread across the United States like wildfire and is now worn by young men and women alike.

West Africans in particular have done a great deal to revive and experiment with cornrowing and hair threading techniques.

The 1960's brought more popularity for cornrowing and hair threading.

Then came the 1980's when Bo Derek stared in the movie "Ten" where she had her hair braided, cornrowed. Being a Caucasian with the cornrowed hair gave other Caucasian girls the idea and the interest in braiding grew and continued through the 1990's.

by Andréa Parsons

References: "Fashions In Hair The First Five Thousand Years" by Richard Corson.
Published 1965 by Peter Owen Ltd., Kendrick Place, London SW7
References: "The World Encyclopedia" 1990 Edition
References: "African Hairstyles (Styles of Yesterday and Today) by Esi Sagay.
Heinemann International Literature & Textbooks, a division of Heinemann Educational Books Ltd., Hally Court, Jordan Hill, Oxford, 0X2-8EJ

Glossary

Bangs:	A fringe of short hair, generally across the forehead.
Base:	The foundation of a section; the section of hair closest to the scalp.
Bobby Pin:	A "U" shaped piece of metal, that has touching sides, and is used for holding hair in place.
Bola Tie:	A western tie, thin like a cord, with metal cone-shaped ends.
Braid:	To weave, interlace, or combine two or more strands together to form a pattern.
Clockwise (C.W.):	Strands wound or twisted around a center in the same direction as hands on a clock move.
Counter-clockwise (C.C.W.):	In a direction opposite to which the hands on a clock move.
Crown:	The top of the head, or parietal area of the head.
Cross-over:	Outside strand, left or right, comes over middle strand.
Feed:	Add hair to the braid, from the hairline or nape area.
Fist:	All fingers closed and wrapped tightly around a strand of hair.
Flowing Nape:	Hair which hangs loose and free at the nape area.
Frontal:	The bone which forms the forehead.
Hairline:	The outline of the scalp, as outlined by the hair around the face.
Hairpin:	Thin "U" shaped piece of metal, sides not touching used for holding hair in place.
Horizontal:	Runs along or parallel to the horizon. Starting at one temporal area, crossing the occipital bone, and finishing at the opposite temporal area.
Index Finger:	Digit next to the thumb.
Intact:	As a whole, all together, a single entity.
Invisible:	Concealed, out of sight, unable to be seen.

Measurements:

1/8"	=	0.3 cm	1/4"	=	0.6cm
1/2"	=	1.3 cm	1"	=	2.5 cm
1 1/2"	=	3.8 cm	2"	=	5 cm
2 1/2"	=	6.3 cm	3"	=	7.6 cm
4"	=	10 cm	5"	=	12.5 cm
6"	=	15 cm	8"	=	20 cm
9"	=	22.5 cm	10"	=	25 cm

Glossary *(Cont'd)*

Middle Finger:	Digit between the index finger and the ring finger.
Nape:	The back of the head, the base of the hairline.
Occipital:	The bone at the lower back of the head; the bone which forms the back of the skull.
One Turn:	Bringing the left outside strand over the middle strand and then right outside strand over middle strand.
Parietal:	The bones which form the sides and top (crown) of the skull.
Pigtail:	A braid made by weaving three strands of hair, without feeding.
Pinch:	The tight grip or squeeze of the thumb and index finger holding a strand of hair.
Plait:	To braid or interweave strands of hair.
Ponytail:	Hair drawn into a single strand or tail.
Roll:	To revolve by turning over and over, generally into a cylindrical shape.
Scrinkle:	Elastic covered with gathered material that forms a circle. Is used to hold a strand of hair in any form.
Section:	A sub-division or portion of hair; to divide or separate a portion of hair.
Sphenoid:	A bone above each ear which joins all bones of the skull together.
Strand:	A group of hairs; one of the major parts of a rope or braid.
Temporal:	Bones which form the sides of the head in the ear region (below the parietal bones).
Tension:	Degree of tightness.
Travelling:	Hair that goes from one point to another, according to a predetermined pattern.
Vertical:	Upright, lengthwise. In braiding, from the frontal area to the nape area.
Vise:	Clamping or tight grasping of a strand of hair by the index and middle finger.
Visible:	Can be seen and observed.
Zygomatic:	The bones which form and give shape to the cheeks.

Bones of the Skull

— The following bones will be mentioned throughout the book. The diagram will help you locate specific areas mentioned.

1. Occipital
2. Parietal
3. Frontal
4. Sphenoid
5. Zygomatic
6. Temporal (see both diagrams)
7. Frontal

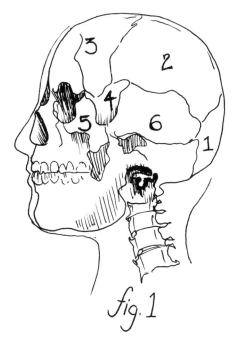

fig. 1

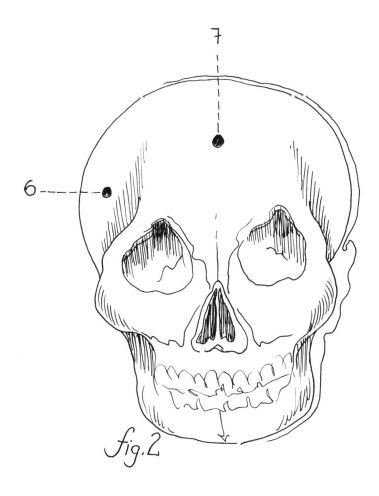

fig. 2

Head Section Terminology

The following terms will be used throughout the book. Familiarize yourself with the terms used for various sections of the head.

1.   Crown Area (see both diagrams)
2.   Front Center of the hairline
3.   Center of the top of the head
4.   Top of ear
5.   Nape area
6.   Base hairline

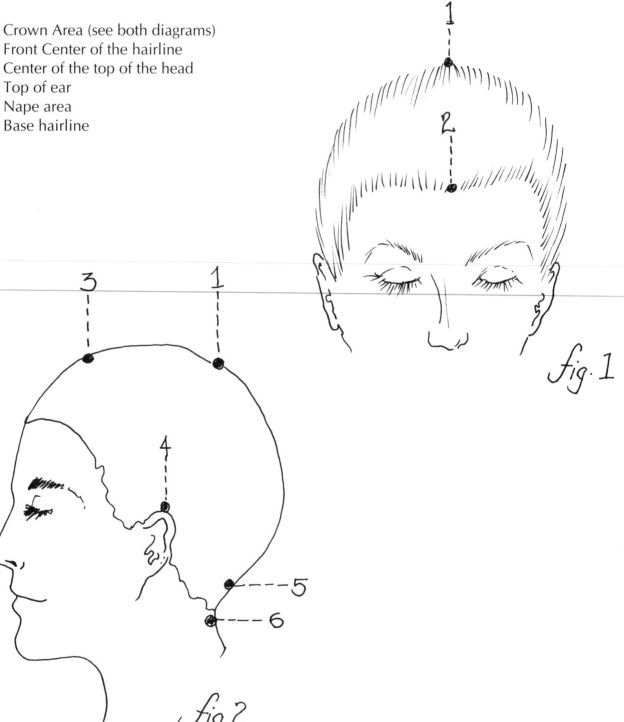

fig. 1

fig. 2

Fingers

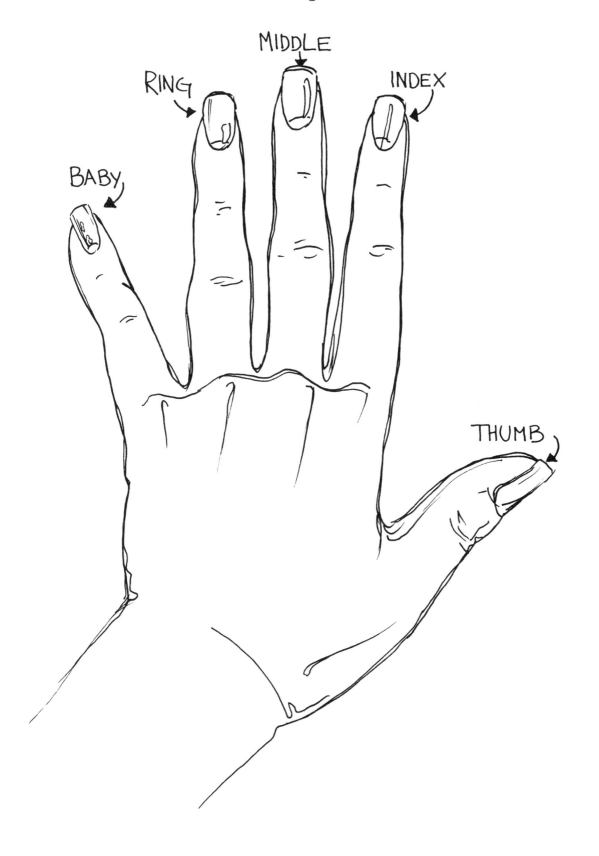

Chapter 1 — Basic Braiding

Basic braiding is a weaving process where hair is combined to form a pattern. The techniques used for braiding hair are essentially the same as those used when braiding anything else. This method is accomplished by taking several sections of hair and crossing them over one another in a definite pattern. As the crossing progresses, plaits of the braid are worked. Each plait is one complete step of the braiding process.

Braiding consists of the following steps:

> Getting Started – Hand Position
> Working The Braid – Plaiting
> Tying Off – Finishing

The basic braids begin with 3 strands, and may be worked in two ways: (1) The English method – strands going over, (2) The Dutch method – strands going under.

1. THE INVISIBLE BRAID

Hand and Finger Position 1

Fig. 1
— Left Hand – Holds strands #1 and #2.
— Right Hand – Has the outside strand #3, which does the travelling, as shown in the next finger position.

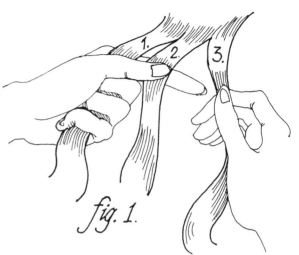

fig. 1.

Hand and Finger Position 2

Fig. 2
— Strand #3 – Crosses over strand #2 and is put into the middle finger.
— With the Right Hand, take strand #2 and position the right index finger under strand #3, with right thumb on top of strand #3.

Fig. 3
— Correctly done, the right hand position will look like Fig.3 once strand #1 is brought over into the middle finger of the right hand.

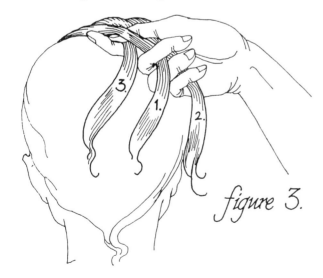

figure 3.

TIPS: After this method has been made skillful, proceed to the **HORIZONTAL INVISIBLE BRAID**.

2. HORIZONAL INVISIBLE BRAID

Fig. 1
— Make Section 'S' as indicated by dots.
— Divide sections into 3 strands. (Fig.1)

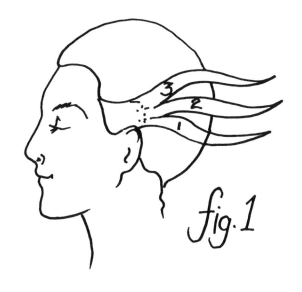

fig.1

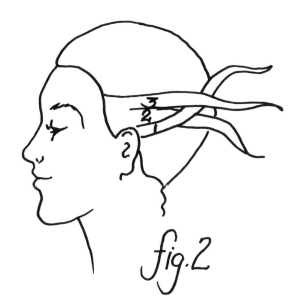

fig.2

Fig. 2
— Strand #1 crosses over strand #2.
— Strand #3 crosses over strand #1. (Fig.2)

Fig. 3
— Feed LEFT strand, from base of hairline (L1), into strand #2 to make #2A.
— Cross #2A over strand #3.
— Feed RIGHT strand from above braid (R1) into strand #1 to make #1B.
— Cross #1B over #2A.
— Feed #L2 into strand #3 to make #3A.
— Cross #3A over #1B.
— Feed #R2 into #2A.
— Cross #2A over #1B.
— Feed #R2 into #2A.
— Cross #2A over #3A. (Fig.3)
— Keep feed strands the same size.

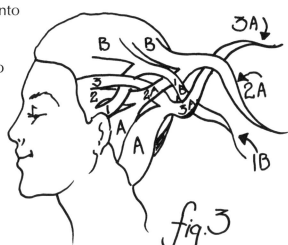

fig.3

Fig. 4
— Feed from 'L' into strand #1B.
— Cross #1B over #2A.
— Feed from 'R' into #3A.
— Cross #3A over #1B.
— Proceed with this method horizontally to right side of head. (Fig.4)

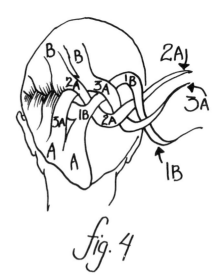

fig. 4

Fig. 5
— The last section to be fed into the braid is the section in front of the right ear.
— Braid the pigtail up to one inch from the end.
— Put an elastic tightly around pigtail.
— Form a coil with the pigtail as shown in Fig.5.
— Secure the coil with bobby pins or strong hairpins.
— The arrows in Fig.5 indicate the correct direction for the coil.

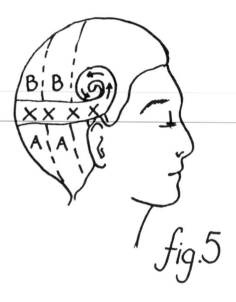

fig.5

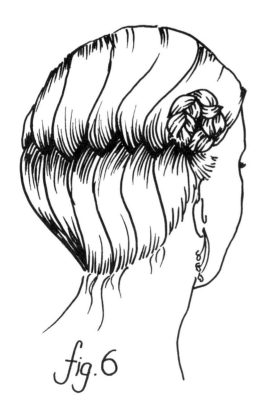

fig.6

Fig.6
— Finished **HORIZONTAL INVISIBLE BRAID**.

3. THE VISIBLE BRAID

Hand and Finger Position 1

Fig. 1
— In making the Visible Braid, both hands are in similar positions.
— Instead of only the index finger under the strands, put the index and middle fingers underneath, side by side.
— RIGHT hand – All fingers are under strand #3.
— LEFT hand – Index and middle finger are under strands #1 and #2.

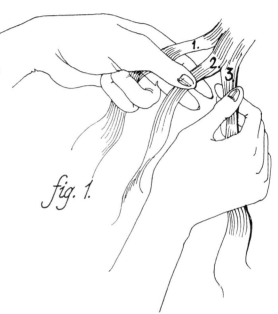

Hand and Finger Position 2

Fig. 2
— Place strand #3 between the index and middle fingers.
— **Always** place the strand so that it lays across the middle finger and under the index finger. This allows hair to be fed into the "little vise" easily, without any problems.

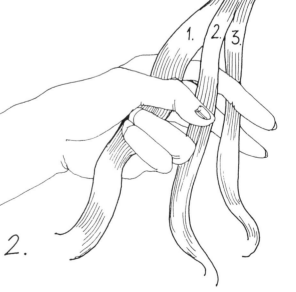

TIPS: After this method has been made skillful, proceed to the **HORIZONTAL VISIBLE BRAID**.

4. HORIZONTAL VISIBLE BRAID

Fig. 1
— Part off section 'S' as shown by dots. (Fig.1)
— Divide the section into three strands.

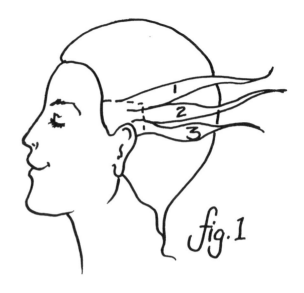

fig.1

Fig. 2
— Put strand #3 under strand #2.
— Put strand #1 under strand #3.
— Feed LEFT strand from base of hairline (L1) into strand #2 to make #2A.
— Put #2A under strand #1.
— Feed RIGHT strand from above braid (R1) into strand #3 to make #3B.
— Put #3B under #2A.
— Feed L2 into strand #1 to make #1A.
— Put #1A under #3B.
— Feed R2 into #2A.
— Put #2A under #1A.
— Repeat this procedure horizontally around head. (Fig.2)

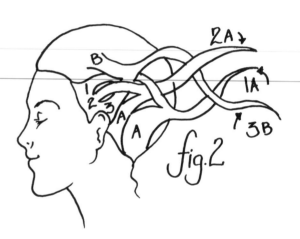

fig.2

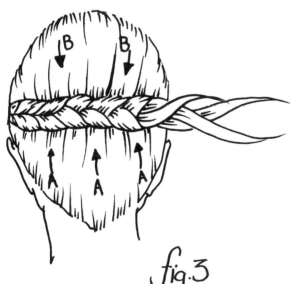

fig.3

Fig.3
— Arrows show direction for feeding from LEFT – 'L' (bottom) and RIGHT – 'R' (top).

— Continue the braid until all the hair has been fed into it.
— Finish braiding the pigtail and secure it with an elastic.
— Put the pigtail in a coil above the right ear.
— The coil will lie above the braid, but close to it.

Fig.4
— Completed **HORIZONTAL VISIBLE BRAID**.

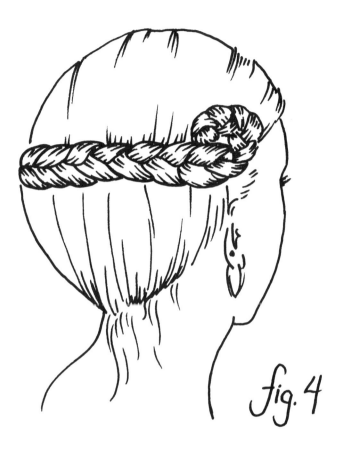

fig. 4

TIPS: When feeding sections into each strand, take same amount of hair. This will give a balanced looking braid.

Chapter 2 — Intermediate Braiding

1. THE HALF BRAID

Fig. 1
— Use **INVISIBLE BRAID** method.
— Section hair as shown by dots.
— Arrow indicates horizontal parting is even with center of right eyebrow.
— Vertical parting begins in front of ear and goes straight up to meet horizontal parting.
— Divide section into 3 equal strands, 1,2,3.

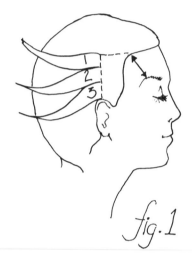

fig.1

Fig. 2
— Strand #3 crosses over strand #2.
— Strand #1 crosses over strand #3.
— Take section 'RF' into strand #2.

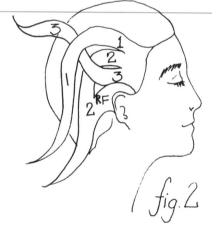

fig.2

Fig. 3
— Strand '2RF' crosses over strand #1.
— Take section 'LF' from left front.
— Feed 'LF' into strand #3.
— Strand '3LF' crosses over strand #2.

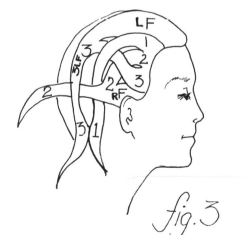

fig.3

Fig. 4

— X's indicate path braid should travel (follow arrows).
— Place hands on the head where braid is to be.
— Bring 'fed in' hair to hand position.

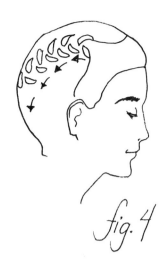

fig. 4

TIP: Do not lower hands from desired location, or braid will lower also.

fig. 5

Fig. 5

— Feed braid from **LEFT ONLY**, from this point on.
— Strand #1 crosses over strand #3.
— Feed from left into strand #2.
— Strand #2 crosses over strand #1.
— Strand #3 crosses over strand #2.
— Feed from left into strand #1.
— Strand #1 crosses over strand #2.

Fig. 6

— Repeat procedure.
— Follow the pattern of the X's.
— Arrows indicate feeding strands.
— Continue to feed from the left of the shaft that hangs down.
— Secure the braid 3 inches from the end with an elastic.

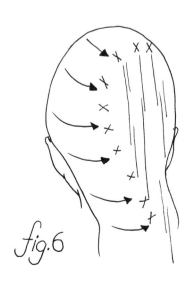

fig. 6

Fig. 7
— The **HALF BRAID** completed.

fig. 7

TIPS: Cover elastic with ribbon, a bow, or barrette.

3 inches = 7.5 cm.

2. BOW BRAID

Figs. 1 & 2
— Make pie-shaped sections 'A' & 'B.'
— Top part is 2 1/2 inches.
— 'C' designates center of nape area.

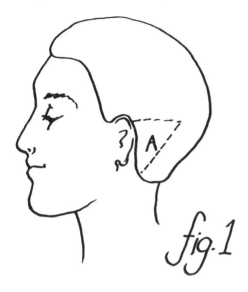

Fig. 3
— Braid each of sections 'A' and 'B' (secure ends with elastic).
— Bring Braids 'A' and 'B' over free hanging hair.
— Tie pigtails as shown.

Fig. 4
— Make bow with pigtails.
— Secure bow in middle with bobby pins **under** bow knot.
— **BOW BRAID** is completed.

TIPS: Cover elastic with **ornamental clasp** that is found on the end of **WESTERN BOLA TIE**. The ornamental clasp may be found in a fabric store.

2 1/2 inches = 6.3 cm.

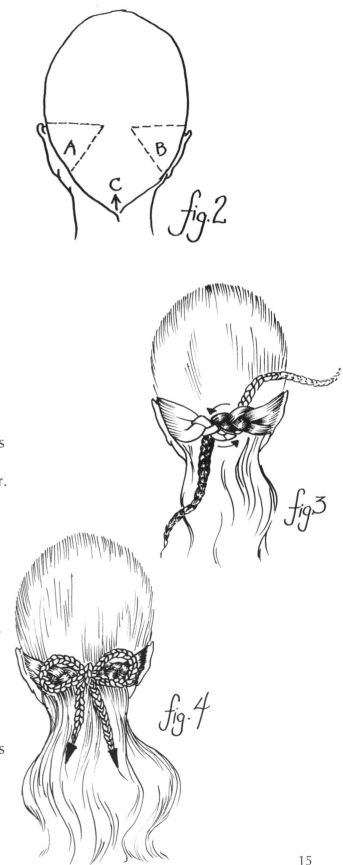

15

3. ZIG ZAG BRAID

Fig. 1

— 'C' indicates center of front hairline.
— Part off section as shown by dotted lines.
— Vertical parts must line up on each side, with outside end of eyebrow.
— Subdivide section into three strands as follows:
— Strand #2 is 1/2 inch wide (1/4 inch on each side of 'C').
— Strands #1 and #3 are of equal width.

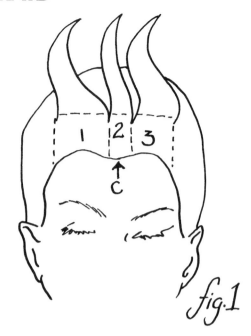

Fig. 2

— Use **INVISIBLE BRAID** method (See directions for **HORIZONTAL INVISIBLE BRAID**).
— Strand #1 goes over strand #2.
— Strand #3 goes over strand #1.
— At this point and to end of instructions,
  'R' = Right strand
  'M' = Middle strand
  'L' = Left strand

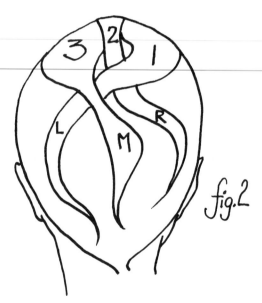

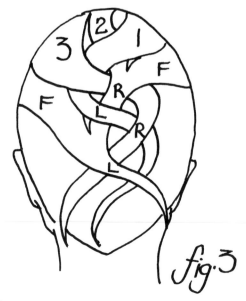

Fig. 3

— Each time an outside strand crosses over, it becomes a middle strand.
— Feed 'R' and cross over middle strand.
— 'L' strand crosses over middle strand.
— 'R' strand crosses over middle strand.
— Feed 'L' and cross over middle strand.

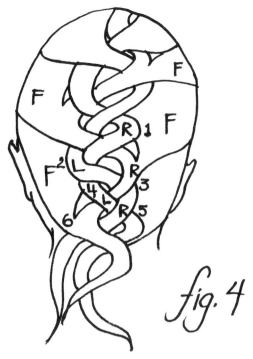

fig. 4

Fig. 4
— 1. 'R' crosses over middle strand.
— 2. 'L' crosses over middle strand.
— 3. Feed 'R'. Cross it over middle strand.
— 4. 'L' crosses over middle strand.
— 5. 'R' crosses over middle strand.
— 6. Feed 'L'. Cross it over middle strand.
— Continue procedure until all hair is fed into braid.
— Using **INVISIBLE BRAID** method, braid tail up to 3 inches from tail end.
— Secure with elastic.
— Cover elastic with ribbon, lace, barrette, or small scrinkle.

Fig. 5
— Completed **ZIG ZAG BRAID**.

fig. 5

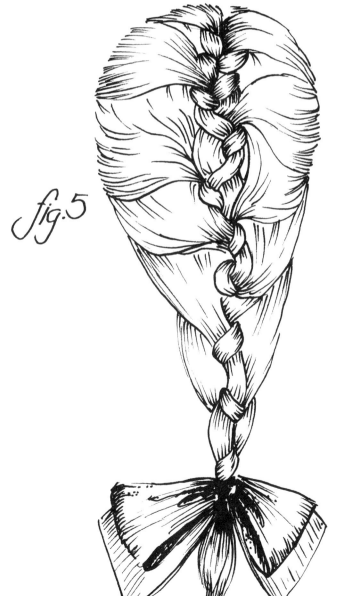

TIP: 1/4 inch = 0.6 cm
1/2 inch = 1.3 cm

4. THE 'C' BRAID

Fig. 1

— Stand on left side of model.
— Tilt her head sideways to her left.
— Make Section 'A' on Right side.
— Make a horizontal part from hairline, at eyebrow level.
— Make vertical part from hairline, back of ear.
— Use **INVISIBLE BRAID** method.
— Feed only from the hairline.
— #1 crosses over #2.
— #3 crosses over #1.

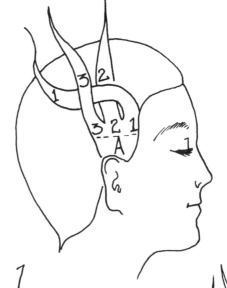

fig.1

Fig. 2

— Feed #2.
— #2 crosses over #3.
— #1 crosses over #2.
— Do not feed #1.
— Feed #3.
— #3 crosses over #1.
— #2 crosses over #3.
— Do not feed #2.
— Feed #1.
— #1 crosses over #2.
— Repeat procedure across top of head to left side.

fig.2

Fig. 3

— X's indicate direction of braiding.
— Arrows indicate feeding from hairline only.

fig.3

Fig. 4

— When braiding nape area, lay right hand on top of 'B' hair.
— Feed from nape area across bottom hairline, bringing feeding up to right hand.
— Braid travels over 'B' hair shaft.
— Secure braid at dot(•).
— The three arrows above dot indicates hairshaft (the last section) goes into braid.
— Secure with elastic.
— Cover elastic with ribbon, bow, or barrette.

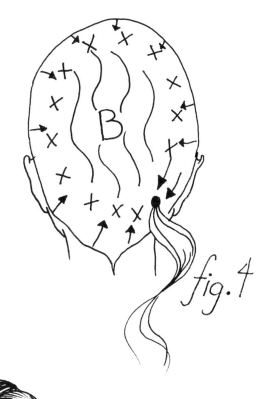

fig. 4

Fig. 5
— Completed **'C' BRAID**.

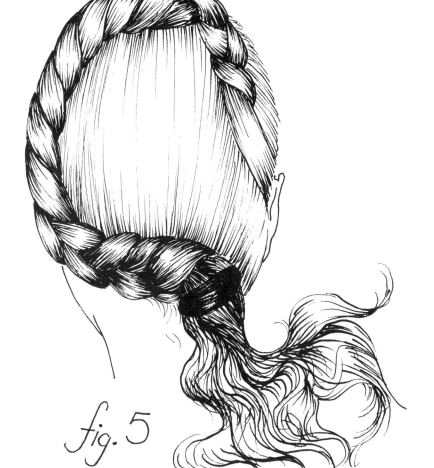

fig. 5

19

5. TASSELS

Fig. 1
— Begin part above center of left eyebrow.
— Continue parting to top of skull – 1 inch above crown area.

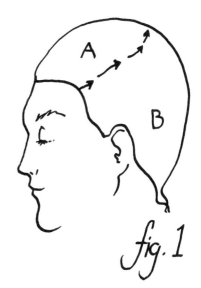

fig. 1

Fig. 2
— On right side, start part at middle of right ear.
— Continue parting to top of head, to join left side parting.

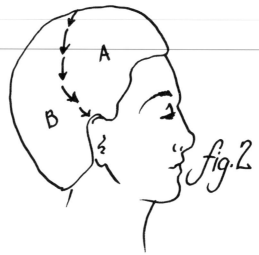

fig. 2

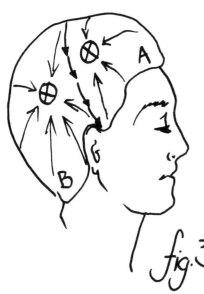

fig. 3

Fig. 3
— X's indicate ponytails 'A' and 'B' should be close to parting.

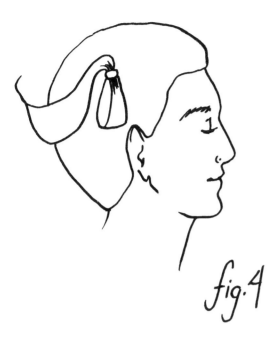

Fig. 4
— Make ponytail from section 'A,' but as hair comes through elastic for last time, do not bring shaft completely through.
— Leave a tail 5 to 6 inches.
— Wind tail around elastic and secure with a bobby pin underneath tassel.
— Repeat procedure for Section 'B.'

Fig. 5
— Completed **TASSELS**.

TIPS: 1 inch = 2.5 cm
                5 inches = 12.5 cm
                6 inches = 15 cm

Always use covered elastics. Rubber elastics damage and break hair.

6. TRIPLE PONY ROLL

Fig. 1
— Part hair as shown in Fig. 1 to make Section 'A' on left side.
— Make a similar section on right side.

Fig. 2
— Pull both sections 'A' and 'B' to back of head.

Fig. 3
— Join 'A' and 'B' together with an elastic.
— Place elastic two finger widths distance from the head.
— Flip ponytail up over elastic and down behind it.
— Pull ponytail down all the way until elastic makes a complete turn.

Fig. 4
— Make second pony roll.
— Part hair from each earlobe to outside of 'AB' tail shaft to make sections 'D' and 'E.'

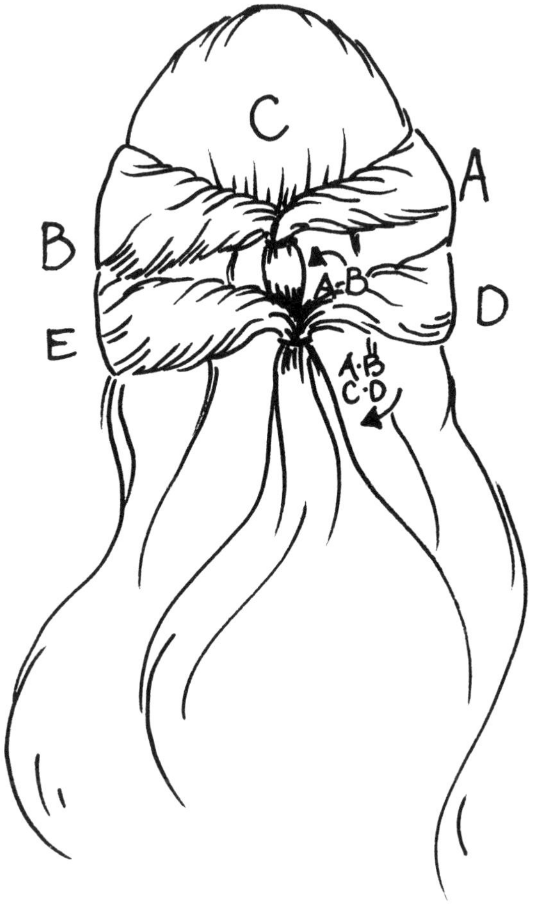

fig. 4

fig. 5

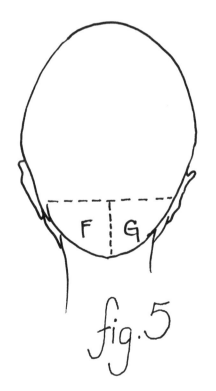

Fig. 5
— Make sections 'F' and 'G' with remaining hair.
— Bring 'F' and 'G' together with an elastic, making sure it is centered at base of skull.
— Flip 'FG' up and over.
— FG lays on 'DE' tail shaft.

Fig. 6
— Finished **TRIPLE PONY ROLL**.

fig.6

TIPS: Elastics may be covered with bows
or small scrinkles. Colored
terrycloth elastics may be used to
create this style.

7. DINOSAUR BRAID

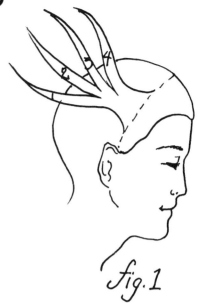

Fig. 1
— 2 inches from forehead make parting from center to ear.
— Divide section into four equal strands.
— Use four strand braiding method, but feed **only** from **right**.
— Right outside strand is **always** fed but left outside is **not** fed.

fig.1

Fig. 2
— Strand #1 crosses over #2, under #3, and over #4.

fig.2

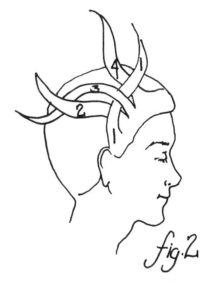

fig.3

Fig. 3
— ***Feed from right side into #2.***
— Strand #2 crosses over #3, under #4, and over #1.
— Feed into #3.
— Strand #3 crosses over #4, under #1, and over #2.
— Repeat procedure, braiding diagonally across head toward left ear.
— Last feed should be just behind left ear.
— Continue four strand method to braid tail.
— Secure tail with elastic, leaving 3 to 4 inches free hair.
— Cover elastic with ribbon, bow, or scarf.

Fig. 4
— Completed **DINOSAUR BRAID**.

fig.4

8. HORIZONTAL TWIST COIL

Fig. 1
— Make section 'A' as shown.
— Direct section away from face and hold horizontally.

Fig. 2
— Hold section 'A' and twist **up**, toward top of head (c.c.w.).
— Keep twisting 'A' until a 9 inch shaft is formed.
— Style will work horizontally around head, toward left side.

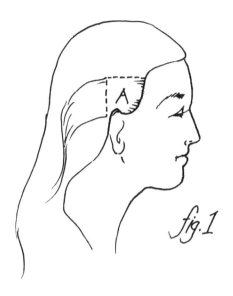

fig.1

fig.2

Fig. 3
— Place index finger as shown.
— Wind twist shaft 'A' around finger to make **tight** coil.

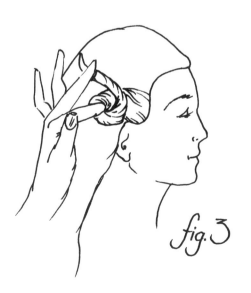

fig.3

Fig. 4

— As coil forms, fasten with large hairpins or bobby pins.
— Insert one end of pin into **bottom** of twisted strand, the other into top of twisted strand.
— Make section 'B' from hairline.
— Feed it into 'A' by wrapping it **over** 'A.'
— Twist 'A' and 'B' up (c.c.w.) together to make one twisted strand.
— Keep twisting up until twisted strand is 9 inches.

fig. 4

Fig. 5

— Make a second coil.
— Fasten coil with hairpin.
— Feed section 'C' into 'AB' strand.
— Twist 'AB' and 'C' together as before.
— Make third coil with twisted 'ABC.'
— Secure third coil (may now require more pins).
— Repeat procedure to make five coils.
— Last coil will rest 2 inches above and in front of ear.
— Keep winding shaft under coil until all hair ends are hidden.
— Secure coil and ends with hairpins.
— Completed **HORIZONTAL TWIST COIL**.

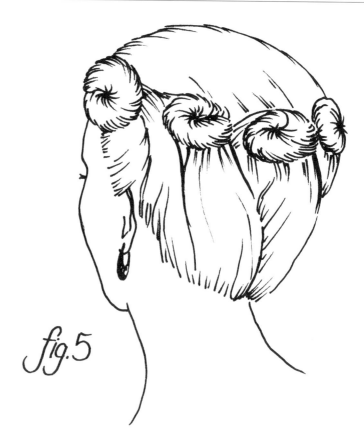

fig.5

TIPS: 9 inches = 22.5 cm
              2 inches = 5 cm

9. SCARF TAIL WRAP

Fig. 1
— Comb all hair to left.
— Make a ponytail at lower left ear.
— Secure with elastic.

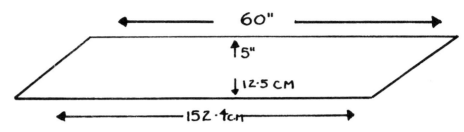

Fig. 2
— Tie scarf end – 4 inches around elastic.
— Tuck short end of scarf under knot.
— Wind scarf around knot, covering both knot and short end.
— Continue winding scarf tightly around shaft.
— Spread scarf width and overlap edges so no hair shows.
— Stop winding 10 inches from scarf end.

fig 3

Fig. 3
— Pull out last loop 'L.'
— Bring scarf tail around back of wrapped ponytail, then over top of left side.
— Scarf tail goes down through top, and out bottom of loop.
— Repeat knot procedure to secure.

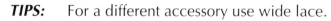

Fig. 4
— Completed **SCARF TAIL WRAP**.

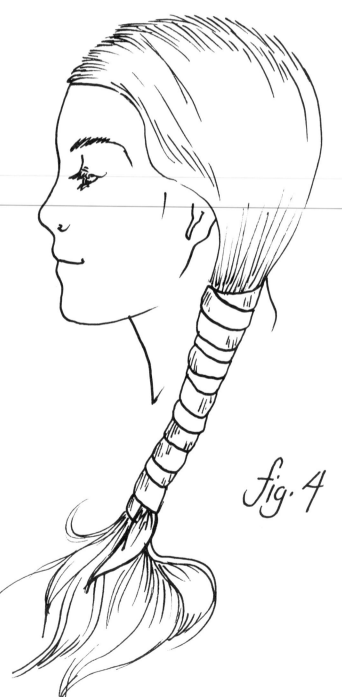

fig. 4

TIPS: For a different accessory use wide lace.

4 inches = 10 cm
10 inches = 25 cm

10. SCARF TAIL WRAP (WITH FLOWING SHAFT)

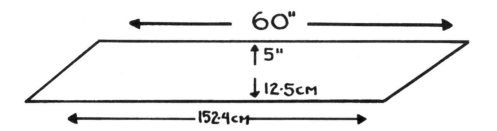

Fig. 1
— Make section 'A.'
— Part 1 – starts at center front area to crown.
— Part 2 – starts at back of right ear lobe to crown, meeting part 1.

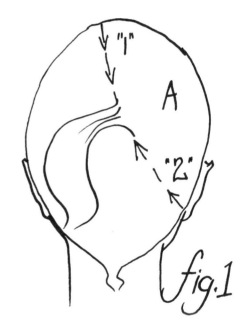

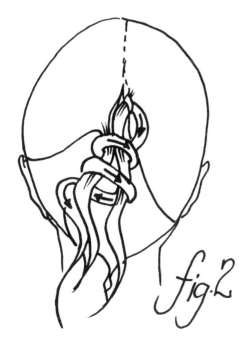

Fig. 2
— Make ponytail with 'A' at crown area.
— Secure with elastic.
— Pull ponytail to left of center part.
— Tie scarf end, 4 inches, around elastic.
— Tuck short end of scarf under knot.

Fig. 3

— Wind scarf up and over knot covering both knot and short end.
— Take section 'B' from top of left ear and add it to shaft 'A.'
— Bring scarf under, up, and over 'AB.'
— Continue winding scarf tightly around shaft.
— Spread scarf width and overlap edges so no hair shows.
— Stop winding 10 inches from scarf end.

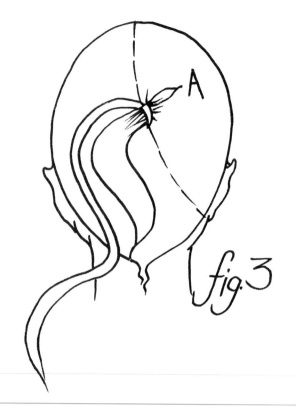

fig. 3

fig. 4

Fig. 4

— Pull out last loop 'L.'
— Bring scarf tail around back of wrapped ponytail, then over top of left side.
— Scarf tail goes down through top, and out bottom of loop.
— Repeat knot procedure to secure.
— Scarf tail should lay on top of wrapped tail.

Fig. 5
— Completed **SCARF TAIL WRAP**
(WITH FLOWING SHAFT).

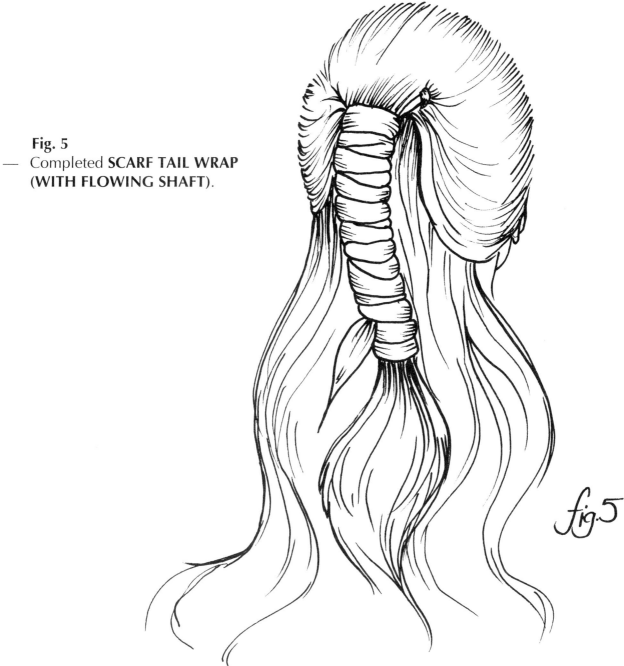

fig.5

TIPS: 4 inches = 10 cm
10 inches = 25 cm

Wide ribbon or lace may be used as an alternative.

Chapter 3 — Advanced Braiding

1. LAUREN'S SHOELACE BRAID

Fig. 1
— Make center part from forehead to nape hairline.
— Tie off right side for later.
— Left side – make pie shaped section 'L.'

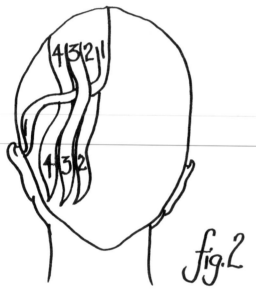

fig.1

fig.2

Fig. 2
— Left side.
— Use **FOUR STRAND** braiding method.
— Divide 'L' into 4 equal strands.
— Begin braid close to center part.
— Strand #1 goes over #2, under #3, and then over #4.
— As braid is formed, keep it 1 inch away from center part.

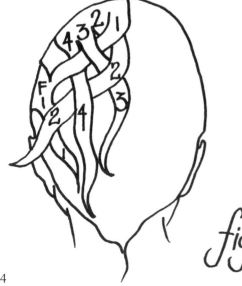

fig.3

Fig. 3
— Leave #1 to left outside of working strand.
— From center, pick up strand #2.
— Strand #2 goes over #3, under #4.
— Take section 'F' from left hairline and feed into #1.
— Put '1F' under #2.

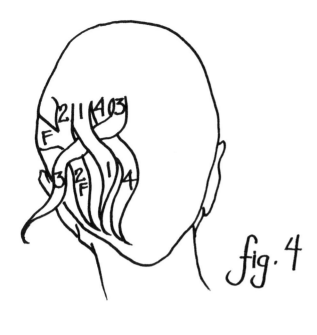

Fig. 4
— Return to center.
— Pick up strand #3.
— Strand #3 goes over #4 and under #1.
— Take section 'F' from left hairline and feed into #2.
— Put '2F' under #3.

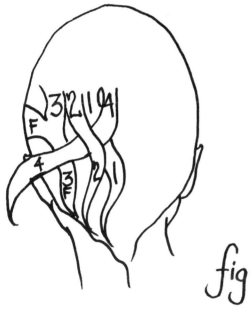

Fig. 5
— Return to center part.
— Pick up strand #4.
— Strand #4 goes over #1, and under #2.
— Take section 'F' from left hairline and feed into #3.
— Put '3F' under #4.

Fig. 6
— Repeat **FOUR STRAND** method.
— To braid tail, continue the same method.
— Secure tail 3 inches from end of shaft.

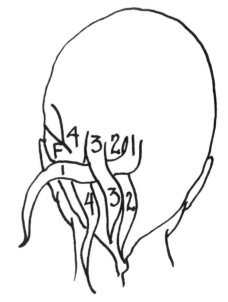

Fig. 7

— Right side.
— Make pie-shaped section as on left.
— Divide into 4 equal strands.
— Strand #1 goes over #2, under #3, and over #4.
— Leave #1 to right outside of working strands.
— Pick up strand #2.
— Strand #2 goes over #3, under #4.
— Take section 'F' from right hairline and feed into #1.
— Put '1F' under #2.
— Repeat same procedure as used on left side, to finish braid.
— Remove left elastic.
— Join the two tails with elastic.

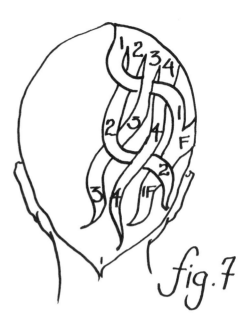

fig.7

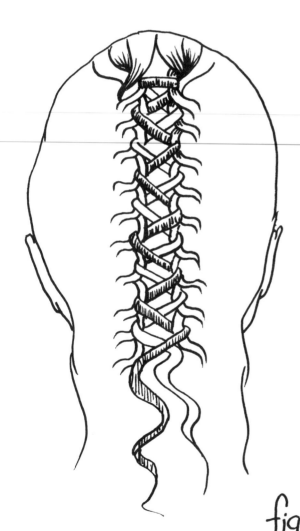

fig.8

Fig. 8

— Shoelace 96 x 1/2 inches.
— Bring shoelace over first two loops 'A' & 'B.'
— Use only loops closest to center part.
— Center shoelace so lengths are equal.
— Lace braid as shown.
— Under loop from center part.
— Over loop from outside.

Fig. 9
— Completed **LAUREN'S SHOELACE BRAID**.

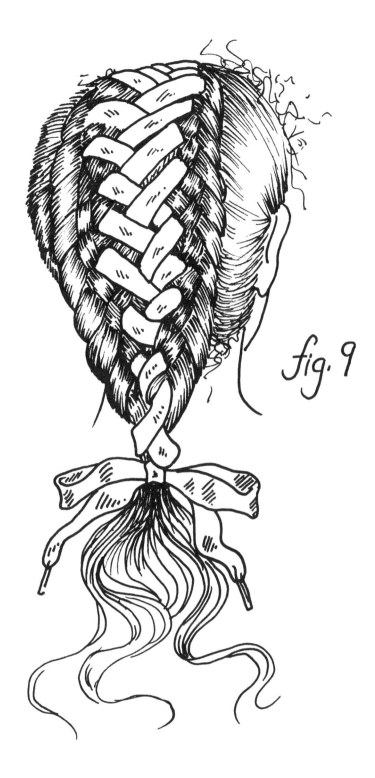

fig. 9

TIP: 1/2 inch = 1.3 cm
1 inch = 2.5 cm
3 inches = 7.6 cm
96 inches = 240 cm

2. REVERSE TWO STRAND

Fig. 1
— Diagram is upside down to show start in the nape at center 'C.'
— Make section as shown by dots.
— Divide the section into 2 strands.

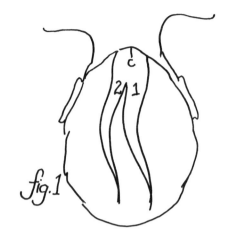

Fig. 2
— Cross strand #1 over strand #2.
— 'F' is the hair section that feeds into a strand.
— Feed left (LF) over strand #1 to join with strand #2 (Makes F2).
— Feed right (RF) over strand 'F2' to join with strand #1 (Makes F1).
— Repeat above procedure to front hairline. (Result – no more hair to feed into the braid.)

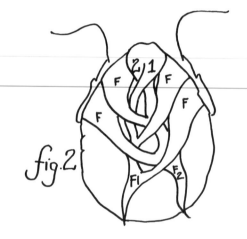

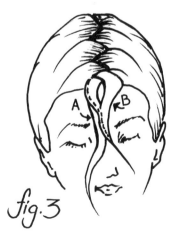

Fig. 3
— Braiding the pigtail.
— 'F1' is strand 'A.'
— 'F2' is strand 'B.'
— Hold strands 'A' and 'B' with good tension – a tightly braided tail keeps the head section of the braid in place.
— Take 1/8 inch section from outside edge of strand 'A.'
— Bring the 1/8 inch section over 'A' to join with strand 'B.'
1/8 inch section must stay on inside of strand 'B.'

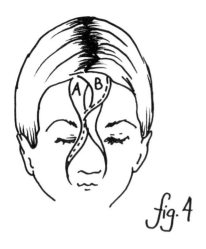

fig. 4

Fig. 4
— Take 1/8 inch section from outside edge of strand 'B.'
— Bring 1/8 inch section over 'B' to join with strand 'A' (1/8 inch section must stay on inside of strand 'A.')
— Repeat procedure until tail is completed – leaving 2 to 3 inches of free hair.
— Secure tail ends with an elastic.
— Tuck tail back and under the hair (Fig. 5).

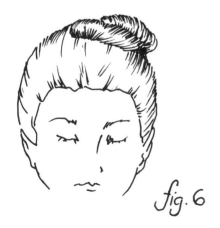

fig. 6

Fig. 5
— Finished **REVERSE TWO STRAND**.

Fig. 6
— Place tail to the left side and center it above left eye.
— Form a coil, keeping the tail on its side to show detail of the braid.
— Secure with hairpins.
— Fig. 6 is **ALTERNATE FINISH**.

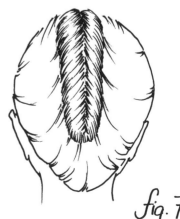
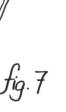

fig. 5

Fig. 7
— Bring tail back, laying it against middle of the head.
— Tuck tail end under braid.
— Secure tail to braid with a barrette.
— Fig. 7 is **ALTERNATE FINISH**.

fig. 7

TIPS: 1/8 inch = 0.3 cm
2 inch = 5 cm
3 inch – 7.5 cm

Put a fancy barrette or bow at the base of the braid.

3. FOUR STRAND CROWN

Fig. 1
— On left side of head, make a horizontal section, as shown by dots.
— Divide section into four strands.

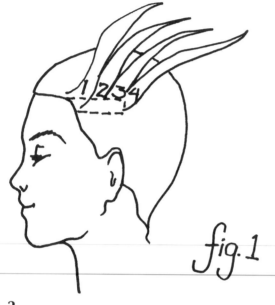

Fig. 2
— Stand at right side of model. Braid over top of head.
— #1 crosses **over** #2, under #3, and **over** #4.
— Feed #2 and cross it **over** #3, under #4 and **over** #1.

Fig. 3
— Keep braiding over top of head.
— Pick up #3.
— Pick up hair from front hairline (F).
— Feed 'F' into #3.
— #3 crosses **over** #4, **under** #1, and **over** #2.
— At this point, #3 will be the left outside strand, #4 will be the right outside strand.
— Feed into braid **only** from the hairline.

Fig. 4

— #4 crosses *over* #1, under #2, and over #3.
— Feed strand #1 and cross over, under, over etc.
— Continue braiding in a circle around head toward the start of the braid.
— Braid until all hairline hair is fed into braid.
— Braid pigtail and secure with elastic.
— Stand pigtail on its side, behind starting braid.
— Tuck tail under starter braid.
— Fasten with pins.

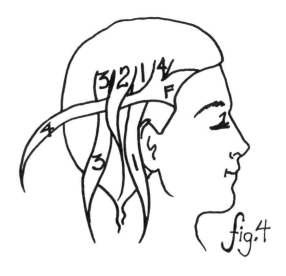

Fig. 5

— 'S'– starting point for **FOUR STRAND CROWN BRAID**.
— 'X's'– the path for braiding arrows – pointing inward – show feeding from hairline only.
— Arrows – inside circle – show braiding direction.

Fig. 6
— Completed **FOUR STRAND CROWN**.

TIPS: Weave a 1/4 inch (.6mm) wide ribbon through the braid for an attractive appearance.

4. JUDY'S CORKSCREW BRAID

Fig. 1
— Comb all hair to the left side of head.
— Gather hair below left ear.
— Twist shaft of hair toward face until tension is very tight.

Fig. 2
— Complete twisting entire hair shaft.
— Hold twisted shaft straight at 'A' with left index finger.
— With Right hand, wind remaining twisted shaft around straight shaft as indicated in Fig. 2.

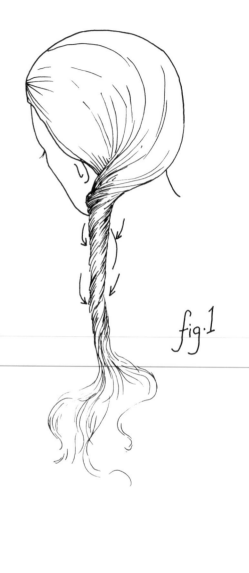

fig.1

fig.2

A —
AREA

Fig. 3
— Actual size of hairpin – 3 inches long.
— Allow 4 to 5 inches at end of shaft to wind tightly around base of twist behind ear.
— End of tail is **under** the base.
— Pin securely with 2 to 3 strong hairpins.

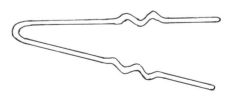

fig.3

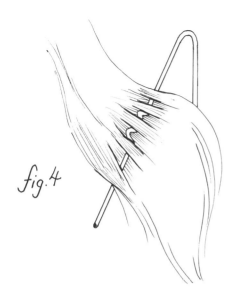

fig. 4

Fig. 4
— Fig. 4 shows how to place hairpins securely.
— Pins will be placed **under** corkscrew so they are **not** visible.
— The hairpin will slide down through the inside of the corkscrew with a weaving movement.

Fig. 5
— Completed **JUDY'S CORKSCREW BRAID**.

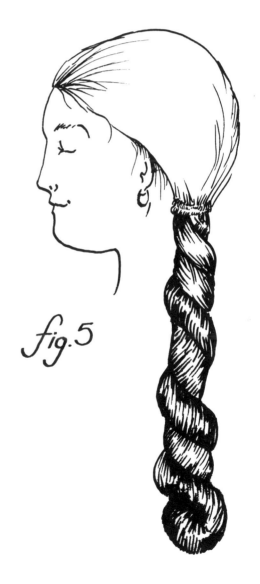

fig. 5

TIPS: 3 inches = 7.6 cm
4 inches = 10 cm
5 inches = 12.5 cm

5. JAN'S STAMPEDE 'S' BRAID

Fig. 1
— 'X' marks the crown area.
— Braid above the 'X.'
— Fig. 1 shows the pattern of the braid.
— Use a **VISIBLE BRAID** method.
— Feed *only* from the side designated by arrows.
— Start the braid at 'S.'
— Feed hair into braid from hairline (see long arrows).
— Around that area of the head, the braid is fed from the **left**.
— 'C' is the continuation of the braid, but now it is fed from the right (middle head section).
— Feed from **right** only, up to 'F.'

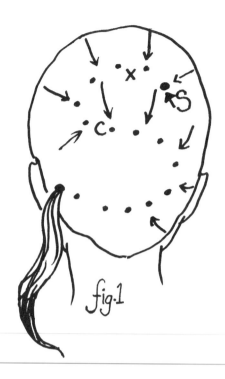

Fig. 2
— At 'F,' feed into braid from the left, but reach **under** braid to get bottom hair.
— Bring baseline hair up, under braid and join with hair just above braid.
— Feed into left outside strand but take under middle strand to add to braid.
— Continue braiding in this manner until back of left ear is reached.
— Secure braid close to the head with an elastic.
— Let rest of hair hang free.

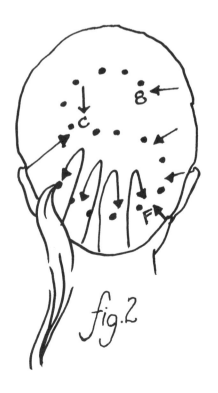

Fig. 3
— Completed **JAN'S STAMPEDE 'S' BRAID**.

fig.3

TIPS: Cover the elastic with an
attractive barrette.

6. THE HORSESHOE BRAID

Fig. 1
— Make a horseshoe parting as shown by dots.
— 'X' is the crown area. Keep the top of horseshoe parting above 'X.'
— 'H' section is the middle area of the horseshoe.
— 'S' section is the starting point of the braid.

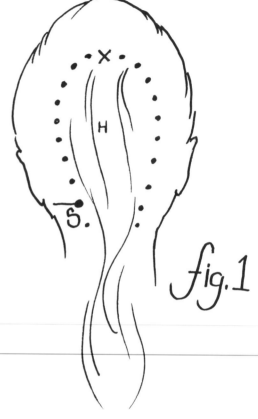

fig.1

Fig. 2
— Have your model face you and bend foreward.
— Take 'S' section and divide into three equal strands.
— Use the **INVISIBLE BRAID** method.
— Place *right* outside strand over middle strand.
— Feed into right outside strand. Cross it over middle strand.
— ***Do not*** feed left outside strand. Just cross it over middle strand.
— Continue this **INVISIBLE BRAID** method, feeding *only* from the outside hairline area.
— Keep the braid on the horseshoe parting as you braid around the head, to the crown area.

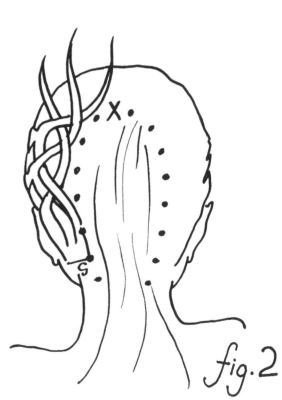

fig.2

Fig. 3

— When 'X' area is reached, model may sit up, as braid will be moving down the head towards the nape.

— Fig. 3 shows the braid rounding the horseshoe.

fig. 3

fig. 4

Fig. 4

— At this stage, the braid is at the middle of the back of the right ear.

— Take a 'feed-in' section from the right hairline (see arrow) then reach **under** the braid to take a small section from the edge of 'H' area.

— Bring strand of 'H' under braid and feed it into braid – from right side.

— Left outside strand now comes over middle, as usual.

— Feed right outside strand from hairline, as usual.

— Go under braid for small section of 'H.'

— Take 'H' under braid to right side and cross over middle strand.

— Left outside strand crosses over middle.

— Repeat this procedure once more.

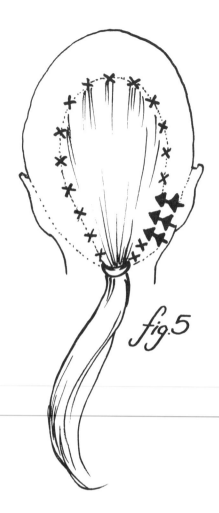

Fig. 5
— The arrows show the three feed-ins from under braid and from right side.
— X's represent braided hair.
— Secure braid at nape with elastic.
— Bring remaining hair of 'H' over elastic twice.
— Wrap 'H' over elastic twice.
— Put 'H' tail to back of braid on its second wrap.
— Stretch elastic out, at back, and pull remaining tail down through it.

fig.5

Fig. 6
— Completed **HORSESHOE BRAID**.

fig.6

7. THE ROPE CROWN

Fig. 1
— Make section 'A' (3 x 1 1/2 inches).
— Stand on right side of model.
— Tilt model's head to right, to begin rope.

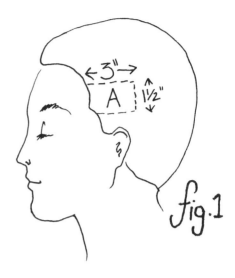

fig.1

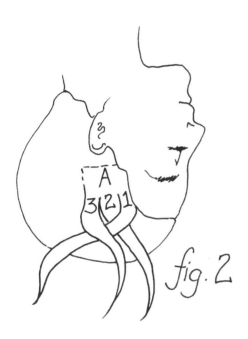

fig. 2

Fig. 2
— Divide section into 3 strands.
— Cross #1 over #2.
— Cross #3 over #1.

fig.3

Fig. 3
— Twist all strands clockwise (to the right).
— Make section 'F.' Feed it into #2.
— Twist #2 clockwise.
— Cross #2 over #3.
— Twist #1 clockwise.
— Strand #1 goes *under* strand #2.
— Right outside strand always crosses *over* middle strand.
— Left outside strand always goes *under* middle strand.
— Everytime a strand is picked up, it must be twisted clockwise.

Fig. 4
— Feed 'F1' into #3.
— Twist #3. Cross #3 **over** #1.
— Twist #2. #2 goes **under** #3.
— Feed 'F2' into #1.
— Twist #1. Cross #1 over #2.
— Twist #3. #3 goes under #1.
— Feed 'F3' into #2.
— Twist #2. Cross #2 over #3.
— Twist #1. #1 goes under #2.
— Note – Left outside strand is never fed.

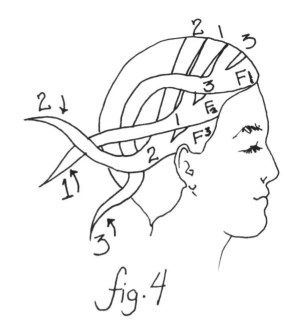

fig. 4

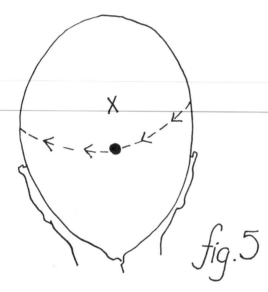

fig. 5

Fig. 5
— Continue procedure around head.
— Keep braid below crown (X), and above occipital bone (O).
— Repeat procedure until all hair from hairline is fed into braid to complete crown braid.
— Braid tail as far as possible to hair ends.
— Fasten with elastic.

Fig. 6
— Tuck braid end **under**, and **inside** rope crown.
— Secure with bobby pins.

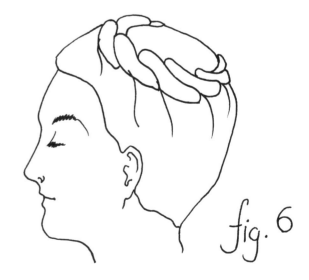

fig. 6

50

Fig. 7
— Completed **ROPE CROWN**.

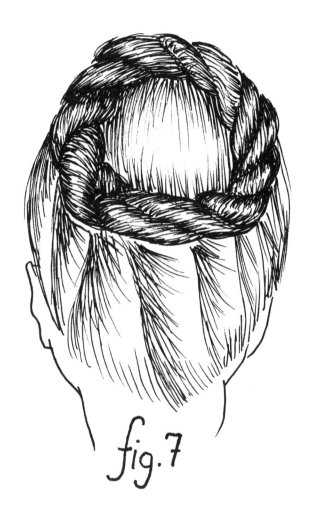

fig.7

TIPS: 3 inches = 7.6 cm
           1 1/2 inches = 3.81 cm

8. JOYCE'S DIAGONAL ROPE

Fig. 1

— Make a square parting as shown by dots (Fig. 1).
— Section 'A' should be even with end of right eyebrow.
— Arrow indicates top line is even with middle of eyebrow.

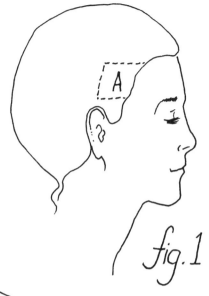

fig.1

Fig. 2

— Divide section into three strands.
— Cross strand #1 over strand #2.
— Cross strand #3 over strand #1.

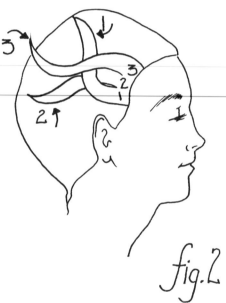

fig.2

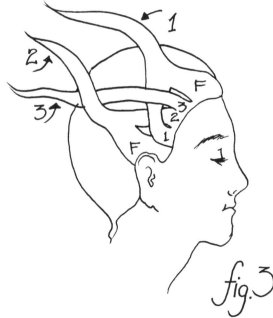

Fig. 3

— Twist all strands clockwise (to your right).
— Make section 'F.' Feed it into #2 (Right side).
— Twist strand #2 clockwise.
— Cross #2 over #3.
— Make section 'F1.' Feed it into strand #1.
— Twist strand #1 and put it **under** strand #2.

fig.3

Fig. 4
— Feed 'F3' into strand #3.
— Twist strand #3 clockwise.
— #3 crosses over #1.
— Feed 'F4' into strand #2.
— Twist strand #2.
— #2 goes **under** #3.

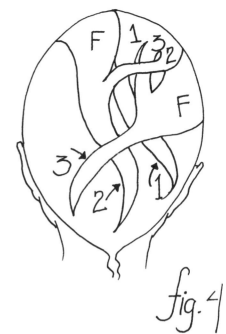

fig. 4

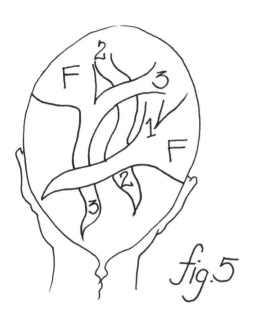

fig. 5

Fig. 5
— Feed 'F5' into strand #1.
— Twist strand #1 clockwise.
— #1 crosses over #2.
— Feed 'F6' into strand #3.
— Twist strand #3 clockwise.
— #3 goes **under** #1.
— Right outside strand always crosses **over** middle strand.
— Left outside strand always goes **under** middle strand.
— Everytime a strand is picked up, it must be twisted clockwise.
— Repeat procedure until all hair from hairline is fed into braid.
— Finish braiding pigtail and secure with elastic.

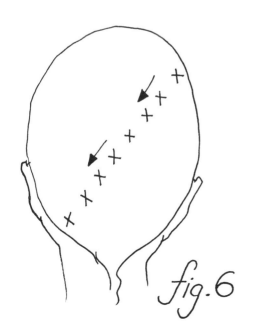

fig. 6

Fig. 6
— 'X's' represent roped hair.
— Arrows indicate direction of braid travel.

Fig. 7

— Completed **JOYCE'S DIAGONAL ROPE**.

fig. 7

TIPS: Cover elastic with ribbon, bow, lace, or scrinkle.

9. FULL TWO STRAND ROPE

Fig. 1
— Follow dots to make section.
— Divide section into two strands 'A' and 'B.'
— Twist strand 'A' to the left (c.c.w.).
— Twist strand 'B' to the right (c.w.).
— Always be aware of direction each strand is twisted.

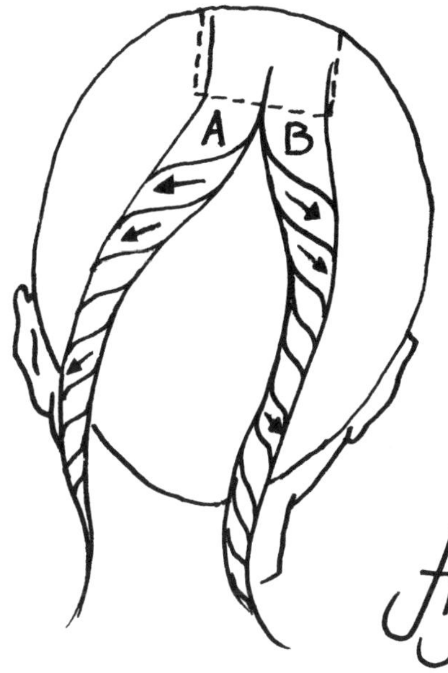

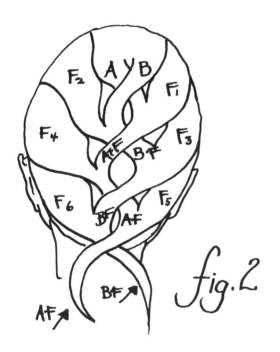

fig. 1

fig. 2

Fig. 2
— Cross 'B' over 'A.'
— Take section from right hairline (F1), sliding up to braid, and feed into 'A' to make 'AF.'
— Twist 'AF' to left (c.c.w.).
— Strands must be twisted in same direction as originally started.
— Feed from left hairline (F2) into 'B' to make 'BF.'
— Twist 'BF' to right (c.w.).
— 'BF' goes **under** 'AF.'
— Feed from right side (F3) into 'BF' strand.
— Twist 'BF' to right (c.w.).
— Feed from left side (F4) into 'AF' strand.
— Twist 'AF' to left (c.c.w.).
— 'AF' goes **under** 'BF.'
— Repeat procedure until all hairline hair is fed into braid.

Fig. 3
- Fasten braid at nape hairline, with an elastic.
- Cover elastic with a barrette, bow, or other accessory as shown in Fig. 3.
- Fig. 3 is completed **FULL TWO STRAND ROPE**.

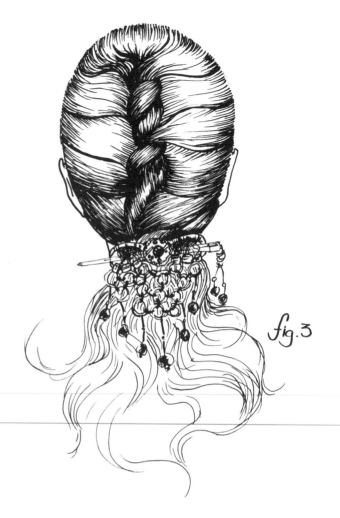

fig. 3

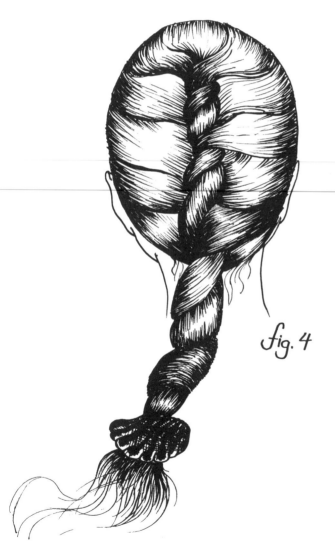

fig. 4

Fig. 4
- Alternate Finish – **TWO STRAND ROPE WITH ROPED TAIL**.
- To make tail, bring right strand over, then under, then over left strand.
- Continue method until roped tail is completed.
- Secure with elastic.
- Finish with barrette, bow, scrinkle, or scarf to cover elastic.

TIPS: Counter-clockwise (c.c.w.).
Clockwise (c.w.).

10. JEAN'S FISH NET

Fig. 1
— Cut long pipe cleaners to make 56 pieces, each 1 1/2 inches long. (Head size will determine number of required pieces)
— Solid line is a center part.
— 'X' is crown area.
— Make a center part – front hairline to crown.
— On **each** side of the part, divide the hair into 4 sections 1 1/2 x 1 inches.

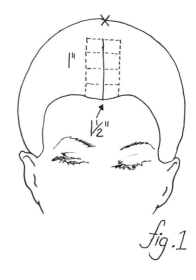

fig. 1

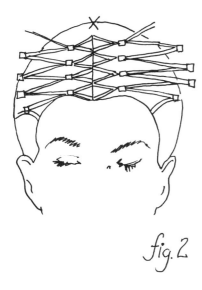

fig. 2

Fig. 2
— About 1 1/2 inches down the strand, wrap pipe cleaner around each of the 8 sections.
— Divide each wrapped strand into 2 strands.
— Majority of strands will be joined with **surface** strands.
— Feed **only** the **front** strands at the hairline.

Fig. 3
— Split strand 'A2' (closest to front hairline).
— Join left 'A1' with small feeding section 'F1' from hairline. About 2 inches down strand, wrap with pipe cleaner at 'B1'. Join right 'A1' with left 'A2.'
— Wrap with pipe cleaner at 'B2.'
— Use same procedure to form 'B3' and 'B4.'
— Using same procedure on right side of head, split all 'A' strands to form 'B' strands.

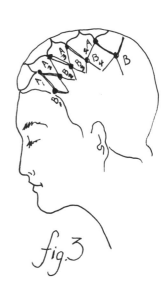

fig. 3

Fig. 4

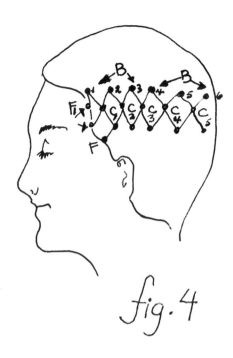

fig. 4

— Return to left side of head.
— Split 'B1.'
— Join left 'B1' with small feeding section 'F1' from hairline.
— About 2 inches down strand, wrap with pipe cleaner at 'C1.'
— Join right 'B1' with left 'B2.'
— Wrap with pipe cleaner at 'C2.'
— Using same procedure, complete entire row 'C' from left around to right side.
— Repeat successive rows down to nape area.

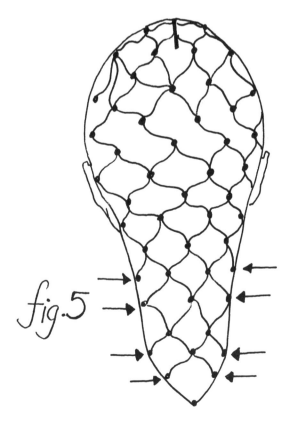

fig. 5

Fig. 5

— Do not feed past nape hairline.
— Work only with existing strands.
— Arrows indicate outside of net.
— Outside left and right strands are no longer split.
— Continue to split and wrap inside strands.
— Wrap last section with 3 inch pipe cleaner.

Fig. 6
— Completed **JEAN'S FISH NET**.

fig. 6

TIPS: Hair must be shoulder length or longer. If preferred, fish net only the skull to nape area.

1 inch = 2.5 cm
1 1/2 inches = 3.8 cm
2 inches = 5 cm

11. SCARF WEAVE

Use a scarf that has the following measurements:

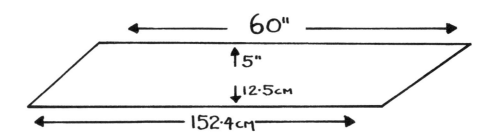

60"
↑5"
↓12·5cm
152·4cm

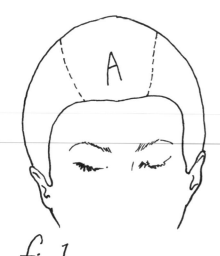

fig.1

Fig. 1
— Make section 'A' as shown by dotted lines.
— Partings should line up with middle of eyebrow on each side.

Fig. 2
— Pull section 'A' to a 45° angle, toward the crown.
— Do not arch 'A' as you secure it with elastic at 'B.'
— Scalp should not be visible at the partings.
— Cover elastic using 4 inches of scarf end.
— Tie a smooth knot.
— Lay short end of scarf on top of ponytail.
— Bring long end of scarf over top to cover small end.

fig.2

Fig. 3

— Take hair section 'RF-1' from right temple area.
— Scarf goes under 'RF-1,' then around, and over top 'RF-1.'
— Bring scarf under strand 'A.'
— Take hair section 'LF' from left temple area.
— Scarf goes over 'LF,' around and under 'LF.'
— Bring scarf over 'A,' and under 'RF.'
— Take hair section 'RF-2' from top of right ear.
— Scarf goes over 'RF-2,' around and under 'RF-2.'

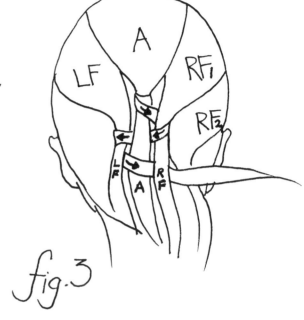

fig. 3

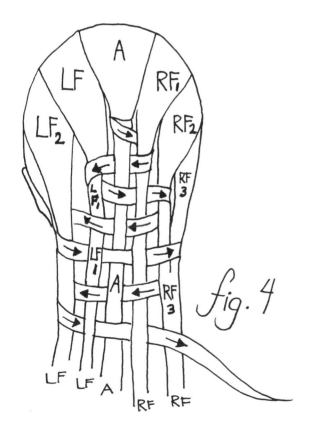

fig. 4

Fig. 4

— Bring scarf over 'RF,' under 'A,' and over 'LF-1.'
— Take hair section 'LF-2' from top of left ear.
— Bring scarf under 'LF-2,' around and over 'LF-2.'
— Repeat weaving method to right side.
— Take hair section 'RF-3' from rear of right ear. Feed into 'RF-3' to make strand thicker.
— Continue sectioning and weaving, as directed.
— Use 4 to 6 hair sections from each side.
— When desired effect is reached, stop adding sections.
— Feed hair into outside strand on left or right.

Fig. 5
— Leave a tail of 4 inches.
— Wind scarf around tail.
— On last wind, bring scarf forward from the back
   (1), slip it under front scarf (2) and out the bottom
   (3).

fig.5

Fig. 6
— Completed **SCARF WEAVE**.

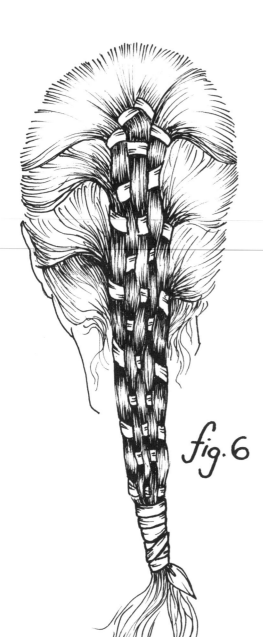

fig.6

TIPS: 4 inches = 10 cm.

Other accessories used for weaving are
ribbon and lace.

Chapter 4 — Ponytail Variations

1. VARIATIONS

Fig. 1 (Variation 1)
— Check index for basic braiding methods.
— At eyebrow level on each side, make partings from hairline back to crown (X).
— Gather section 'A' at X.

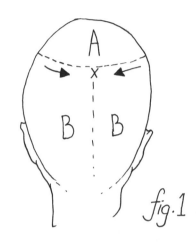

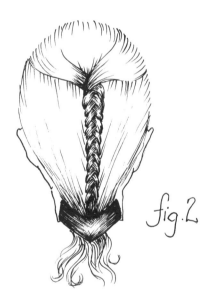

Fig. 2
— Use **INVISIBLE BRAID** method to braid ponytail to nape.
— Gather together remaining hair (B) at nape area.
— Join tail of 'A' and 'B' with elastic.
— Cover elastic with ribbon, lace bow, or scrinkle.

Fig. 3 (Variation 2)
— Section hair as in Fig. 1.
— Use **THREE STRAND ROPE** method to braid ponytail to nape.
— Join 'A' and 'B' tails – as in Fig. 2.
— Cover elastic with cord.
— Knot the cord and let ends hang loose.

Fig. 4 (Variation 3)
— Section hair as in Fig. 1.
— Use **TWO STRAND BRAID** method to braid ponytail to nape.
— Join 'A' and 'B' tails – as in Fig. 2.
— Cover elastic with barrette.

fig. 4

fig. 5

Fig. 5 (Variation 4)
— Section hair as in Fig. 1.
— Use **DINOSAUR BRAID** method (4 strands).
— Join 'A' and 'B' tails as in Fig. 2.
— Cover elastic with large, plain barrette or bow.

Fig. 6 (Variation 5)
— Section hair as in Fig. 1.
— Use **LOW SINGLE TIE KNOT** method.
— Continue knots to nape.
— Join 'A' and 'B' tails as in Fig. 2.
— Cover elastic with lace bow.

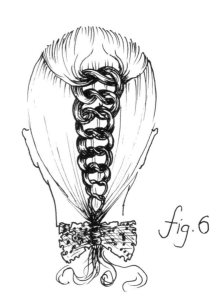

fig. 6

2. HIGH PONYTAIL SPLIT

Fig. 1
— Section hair from top of each ear to crown area (see Fig. 1).
— Ponytail should lay on part and show no scalp.

Fig. 2
— With section 'A' make ponytail at crown area.
— Slide elastic down 1/4 inch on ponytail.
— To split ponytail, place index finger under ponytail between elastic and head.
— Use middle finger to hold right section separate from left section.

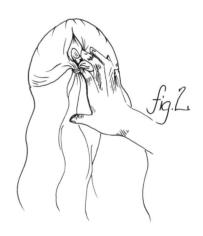

Fig. 3
— Bring ponytail up and grab it with index finger.
— With index finger around ponytail, pull tail through split area and down under the elastic.
— Pull tail until elastic flips over and under.
— A roll will now appear on both sides.

Fig. 4
— Place a second elastic 3 inches down from first elastic.
— Split section between the two elastics.
— Slip ponytail through split area.
— Pull tail down until elastic flips over completely. (Fig. 4)

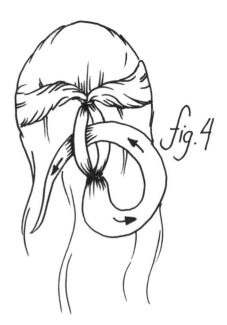

Fig. 5
— Finished **HIGH PONYTAIL SPLIT**.

TIPS: Cover elastic with bow or small scrinkle.

        1/4 inch = .6 mm
        3 inches = 7.6 cm

3. LOW PONYTAIL SPLIT

Fig. 1
— Gather the hair at the base of the skull (nape area) to make a ponytail (Fig. 1).
— Slide the elastic down 1/4 inch on ponytail.
— To split ponytail, place index finger under ponytail between elastic and head.
— Use middle finger to hold right section separate from left section.

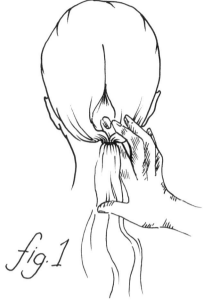

fig. 1

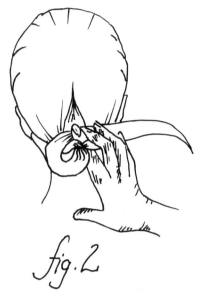

fig. 2

Fig. 2
— Bring ponytail up and grab it with index finger.
— With index finger around ponytail, pull tail through split area and down under elastic.
— Pull tail until elastic flips over and under (Fig. 3).

fig. 3

Fig. 3
— A roll will appear on both sides.
— Cover elastic with a bow.

Fig. 4 (Another Preference)

— To hide elastic, flip the tail over a second time.
— Do **not** let elastic turn this time.
— Slide bobby pin under the top of the roll ('A' in Fig. 4).

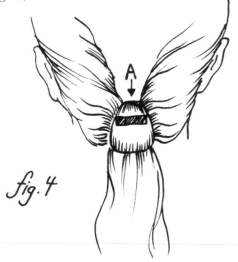

fig. 4

Fig. 5

— Completed **LOW PONYTAIL SPLIT**.

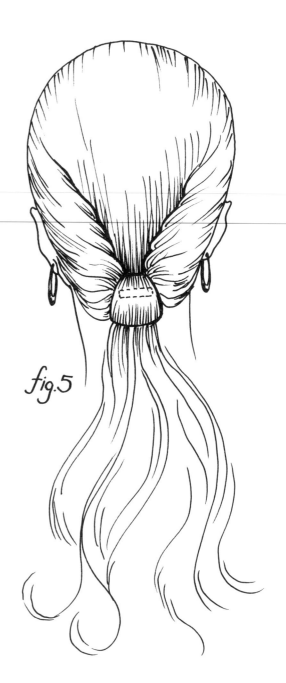

fig. 5

4. LOW BARRETTE SPLIT

Fig. 1
— Gather all hair at base of skull.
— Place a barrette around gathered hair.
— Slide barrette one inch down the shaft (Fig. 1).

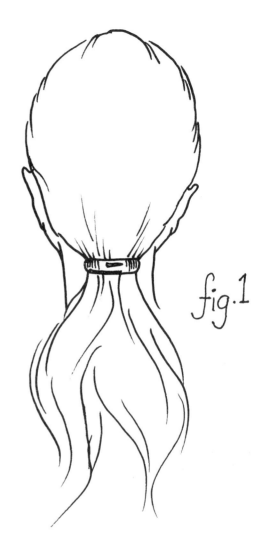

fig.1

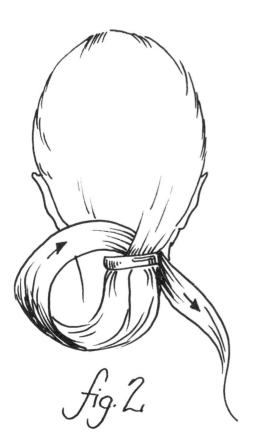

fig. 2

Fig. 2
— Place left hand under barrette.
— With left index finger split hair above barrette.
— With right hand swing end of hair shaft up, catching it with left index finger.
— Pull hair shaft through split until barrette makes a complete turn (Fig. 2).
— If barrette does not turn all the way, slide it down further to allow more freedom to turn.

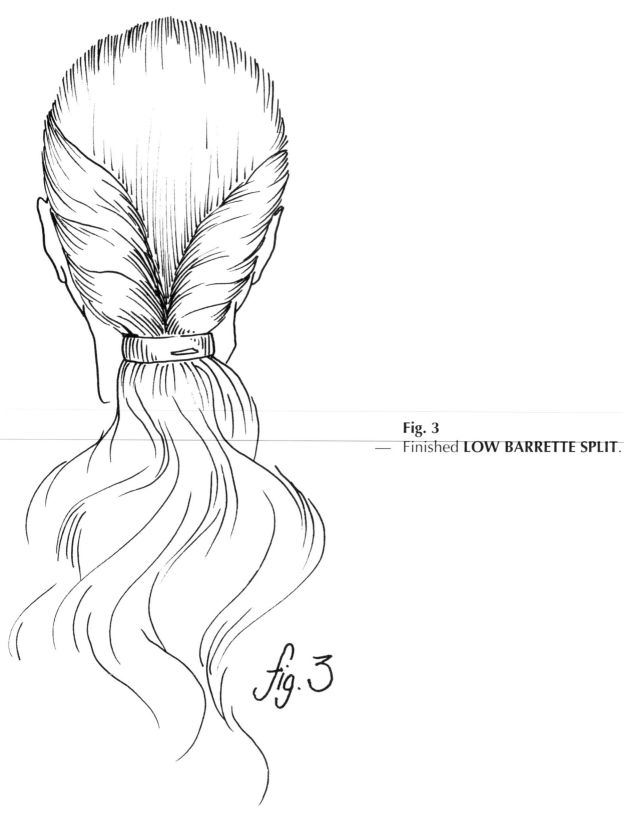

Fig. 3
— Finished **LOW BARRETTE SPLIT**.

fig. 3

TIPS: A barrette 1/2 inch (1.3 cm) wide makes a fuller roll.

5. FLINN SPLIT

Fig. 1
— **FLINN SPLIT** is a variation of **HIGH PONYTAIL SPLIT**.
— Fig. 1 is a **PONYTAIL SPLIT**.
— Follow all directions for this style from beginning to end (see style for **HIGH PONYTAIL SPLIT**.

fig. 1

Fig. 2
— Take free hanging bottom section and part in center to make 'L' and 'R.'
— Pull 'L' and 'R' through the split as shown.
— Stretch the second elastic behind the tail and put 'L' and 'R' through it. (This secures 'L' and 'R' so there is no movement or slipping).
— Pull down on 'L' and 'R' tail strands so that sections lay snuggly against head.
— Put a barrette at base area.

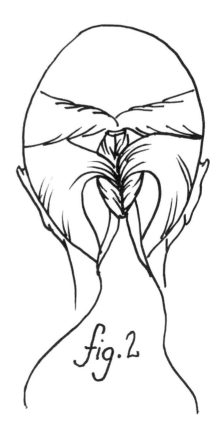

fig. 2

Fig. 3
— Completed **FLINN SPLIT**.

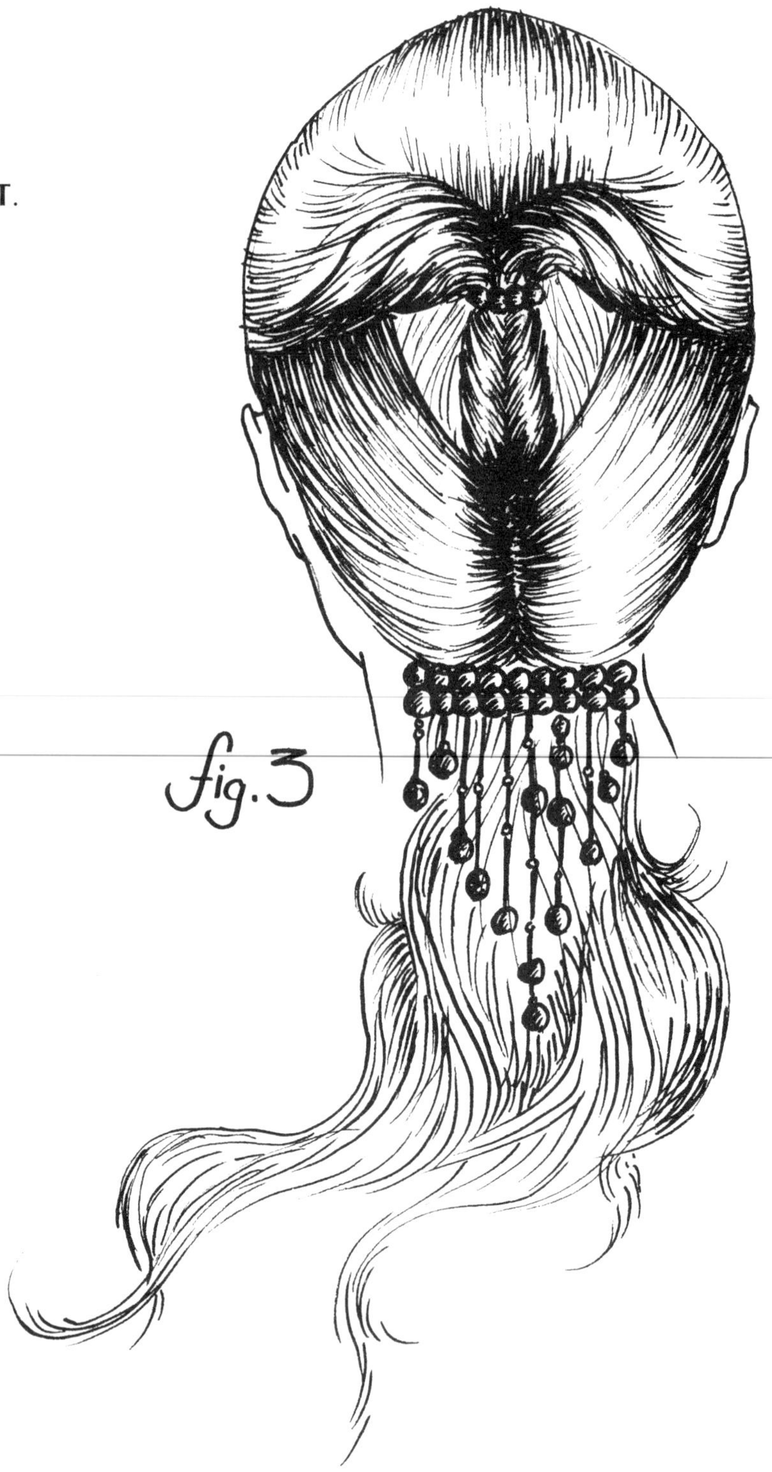

fig.3

Chapter 5 — Styles for Men

— *See index for directions for these finished styles.*
— *Secure ponytail with leather strings, terry towel elastics, shoe strings, silver or gold plain barrettes 2 inches (5 cm) long.*

1. TWO STRAND PONYTAIL

Fig. 1

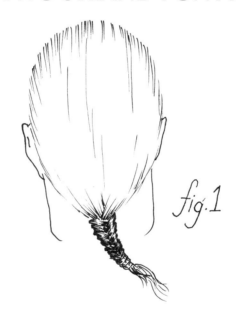

fig.1

2. THREE STRAND ROPE TAIL

Fig. 2

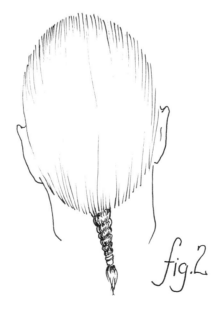

fig.2

3. FULL THREE STRAND ROPE

Fig. 3
— Entire head is braided using the **THREE STRAND ROPE** method.

fig. 3

4. FOUR STRAND PONYTAIL

Fig. 4

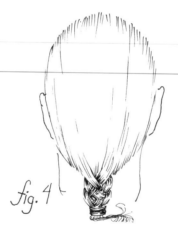

fig. 4

5. VERTICAL INVISIBLE BRAID

Fig. 5
— Entire head is braided using the **INVISIBLE BRAID** method.

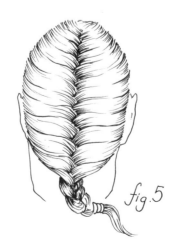

fig. 5

Scarf Tail Wrap
Page 29

Lauren's Shoelace Braid
Page 34

Judy's Corkscrew Braid

Page 42

Jan's Stampede "S" Braid
Page 44

The Horseshoe Braid

Page 46

79

Joyce's Diagonal Rope
Page 52

Jean's Fish Net
Page 57

81

Scarf Weave
Page 60

82

Andréa's Diagonal Scrinkle Braid

Page 87

83

Reverse Scrinkle

Page 105

84

Lindsay's Two Sided Twist Braid

Page 108

85

Jennifer's Triple Ponytail Knots
Page 119

Chapter 6 — Scrinkles

1. ANDRÉA'S DIAGONAL SCRINKLE BRAID

Fig. 1
— Scrinkle – a piece of elastic covered with gathered material (Fig. 1).
— Scrinkles should stretch to 8 inches to do a style that includes the entire head of hair.
— Scrinkles come in various lengths.

Fig. 2
— Take hair section 'A' from front hairline to top of head.
— Insert hair through scrinkle.

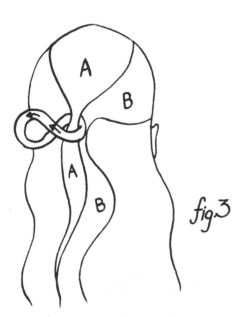

Fig. 3
— With left hand, twist scrinkle once.
— Continuous section is on top (Fig. 3 – see arrows).
— Put left thumb and middle fingers (not entire hand), through scrinkle at 'X.'
— Grab tail 'A' and hold.

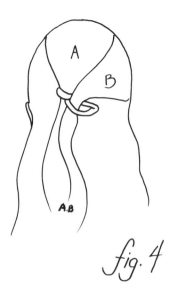

Fig. 4
— With right hand, take section 'B' from right ear area.
— Feed section 'B' into tail of section 'A' to form 'AB.' (Fig. 3)
— Left hand holds 'AB.'
— With right hand pull scrinkle over tail 'AB.'
— Twist scrinkle once.
— Continuous section lies on top.
— Put right thumb and fingers through scrinkle.
— Hold 'AB' with right hand.

fig. 4

Fig. 5
— Take section 'C' from left side of head (just above ear).
— Feed section 'C' into 'AB' to make 'ABC.'
— Right hand now holds 'ABC.'
— With left hand, pull scrinkle over 'ABC' tail.
— Twist scrinkle with left hand.
— Continuous section lies on top.
— Put left thumb and fingers through scrinkle.
— Hold 'ABC' with left hand.

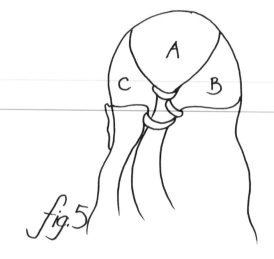

fig. 5

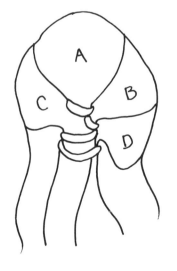

fig. 6

Fig. 6
— Take section 'D' from right side of head.
— Feed section 'D' into 'ABC' to make 'ABCD.'
— Left hand now holds 'ABCD.'
— With right hand, pull scrinkle over 'ABCD' tail.
— Twist scrinkle with right hand.
— Continuous section lies on top.
— Put right thumb and fingers through scrinkle.
— Right hand now holds 'ABCD.'

Fig. 7
— Take section 'E' from left and right side.
— Feed section 'E' into 'ABCD' to make 'ABCDE.'
— Right hand now holds 'ABCDE.'
— With left hand, pull scrinkle over 'ABCDE' tail.
— Twist scrinkle once and then again.

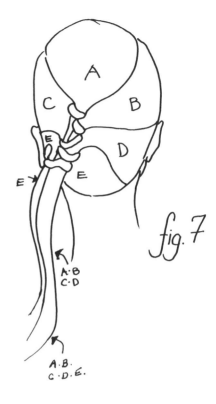

fig. 7

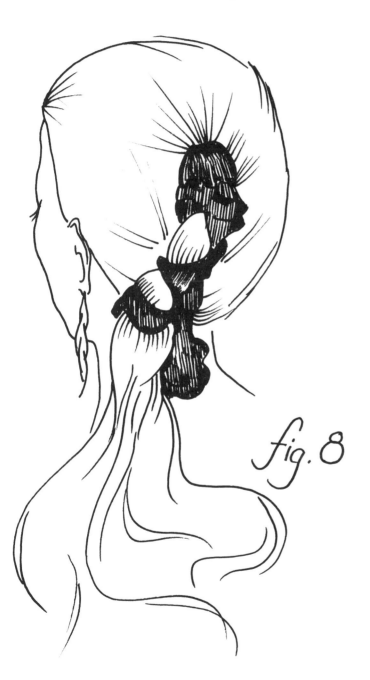

fig. 8

Fig. 8
— Completed **ANDRÉA'S DIAGONAL SCRINKLE BRAID.**

TIPS: Hands set up the direction for hair to follow. Thus, to achieve a certain direction, ***always place your hand at the desired location.***

2. VERTICAL SCRINKLE BRAID WITH FLOWING SHAFT

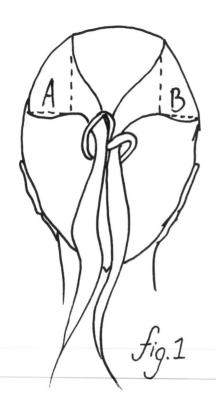

Fig. 1
— Make section 'A' on left side.
— Make 'A' low side part on the left side.
— Part hair on top from temple to corner of the side part.
— Part hair on top from temple to corner of side part.
— Make section 'B' on right side using same method.
— Put scrinkle around 'A.'
— Twist scrinkle once.
— Put 'B' strand through scrinkle, joining it with 'A.'

Fig. 2
— Twist scrinkle.
— On left, make section 'C' (See Fig. 2).
— While holding section 'AB,' bring section 'C' through scrinkle and join it with section 'AB.'
— Twist scrinkle around 'ABC.'

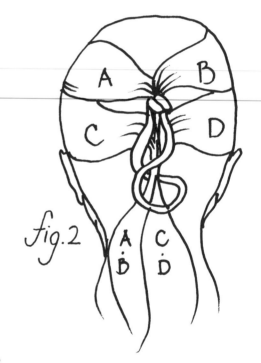

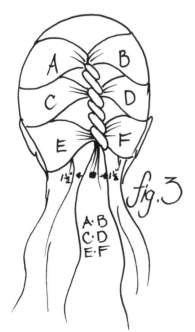

Fig. 3
— On right side.
— Add 'D' strand to 'ABC' and twist scrinkle around 'ABCD.'
— Continue this method.
— 'E' and 'F' sections are taken 1_ inches (3.81 cm) from the middle.

Fig. 4
— Completed **VERTICAL SCRINKLE BRAID WITH FLOWING SHAFT**.

fig. 4

Fig. 5
— **VARIATION VERTICAL SCRINKLE**
— Bring loose tail through scrinkle, leaving 6 inches (15 cm) for wrap.
— Fig. 5 illustrates.
— Wrap tail around style at nape area.
— Secure tail at back with bobby pin or secure tail by bringing it through scrinkle again.

fig.5

Fig. 6
— Completed **VARIATION VERTICAL SCRINKLE**.

fig.6

3. THE GENIE SCRINKLE

Fig. 1
— Use a scrinkle 1 1/2 inches (3.8 cm) wide with a stretch capacity of 9 inches (22.5 cm).
— Part hair along dotted lines to make sections 'A' and 'B.'
— Section 'C' hangs down freely.

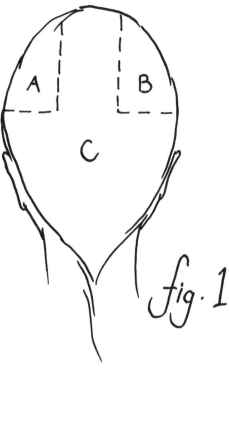

Fig. 2
— Put scrinkle around 'A.'
— Twist the scrinkle once.
— Put 'B' through scrinkle. Combine it with 'A.' Twist the scrinkle once. 'A' and 'B' are now one strand.

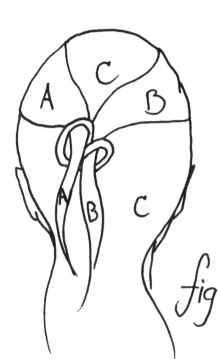

Fig. 3
— Take section 'D' (left ear lobe to top of ear).
— Put 'D' through scrinkle. Add it to 'AB' strand.
— Twist scrinkle once.
— For 'E' section make a part starting at left side of center nape area.
— Put 'E' section through scrinkle. Add 'E' to 'ABD' strand.
— Twist scrinkle once.
— If scrinkle seems loose then pull the strand, 'ABDE,' through again, and twist scrinkle once more.
— Repeat until scrinkle is secure.

93

Fig. 4
— Finished **GENIE SCRINKLE**.

fig.4

94

4. THREE STRAND SCRINKLE

Fig. 1
— Scrinkle size – 1 inch (2.5 cm) wide, stretched 8 inches (20 cm).
— Make sections 'A,' 'B,' 'C.'

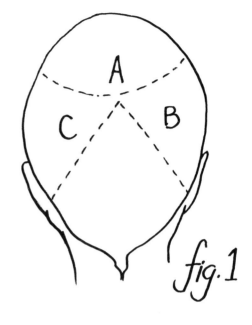

Fig. 2
— Section 'A' is from left and right temple area to crown.
— Twist scrinkle once.
— Keep only fingers of left hand through scrinkle loop.
— Hold shaft of 'A' in palm.

Fig. 3
— Bring 'B,' from middle of right ear, up to center, below crown area.
— Join 'B' and 'A.'
— Pull 'AB' through scrinkle.
— Twist scrinkle once.
— Put **only fingers** through scrinkle.
— Pick up shaft 'AB' with hand holding scrinkle.

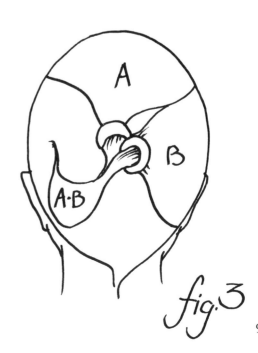

Fig. 4
— Bring 'C,' from middle of left ear, up to center.
— Join 'C' with 'AB.'
— Pull 'ABC' through scrinkle.
— Twist scrinkle once.
— Pull 'ABC' through scrinkle a second time.
— Spread out scrinkle by pulling top up, and bottom down.
— This allows more hair to show through.

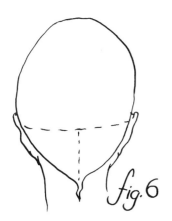

Fig. 5
— Completed **THREE STRAND SCRINKLE**.

Fig. 6
— **VARIATION:** *LOW* **THREE STRAND SCRINKLE**.
— Section as indicated.
— Follow above instructions.

TIPS: A silk or satin scrinkle may be too slippery to hold hair. A cotton scrinkle will hold hair more securely and stay in place. Use own judgement according to style.

5.   SIDE SCRINKLE TAIL

Fig. 1
— Scrinkle – must stretch to 7 inches (17.5 cm).
— 'C' is center of head, from forehead to nape.
— Make section 'B' – see dotted line.
— Make section 'A' – see dotted line.

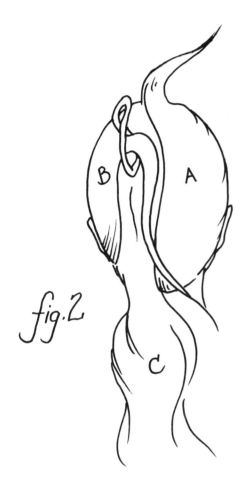

fig. 1

Fig. 2
— Put scrinkle around section 'B.'
— Give it a twist.
— Put fingers of left hand part way through scrinkle.
— Bring 'A' over to 'B' to make one strand.
— Pull scrinkle over strand 'AB.'

fig. 2

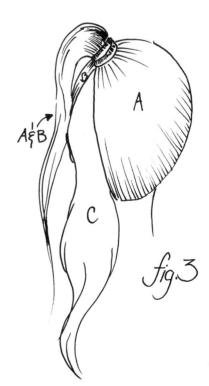

fig. 3

Fig. 3
— Twist scrinkle once.
— Right hand should now be holding hair shaft.
— Twist scrinkle once more pulling it over the other material and to the base of the gathered tail.
— Tail should line up with back of left ear and even with left side part.

Fig. 4
— Completed **SIDE SCRINKLE TAIL**.

fig. 4

6. SCRINKLE BASE KNOT

Fig. 1
— Section hair as shown.
— Section 'L' and 'R' are working sections.
— Section 'C' hangs free under 'L' and 'R.'

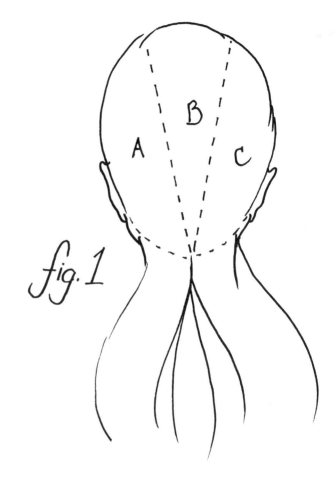

fig.1

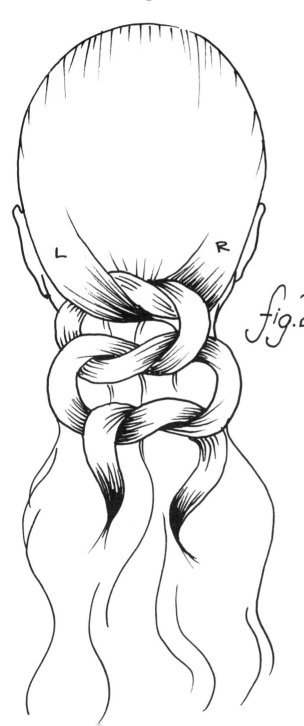

fig.2

Fig. 2
— Bring 'L' over 'R' to make a tie (1).
— Bring 'L' over and around 'R,' up through loop hole to make second tie.
— Take 'R' over 'L.'
— Let 'L' continue over 'R,' thus going through loop hole from top.
— As they are made, tighten ties with firm tension.
— At last tie, secure base with scrinkle.

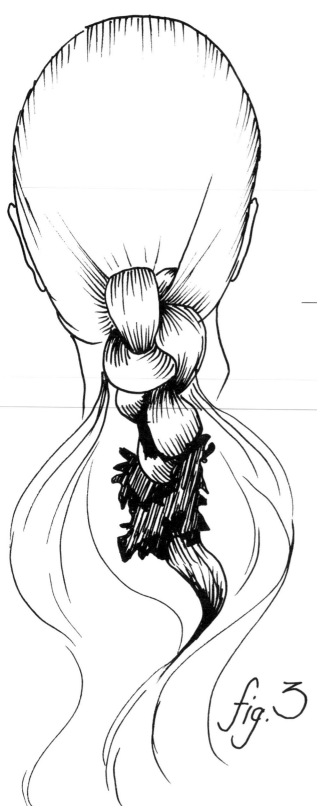

Fig. 3
— Completed **SCRINKLE BASE KNOT**.

fig. 3

7. SCRINKLE PONYTAIL

Fig. 1
— Scrinkle – 8 inches (20 cm)
— Make ponytail and put scrinkle around it.
— Ponytail may be on any area of head.

fig.1

fig.2

Fig. 2
— Use a second scrinkle (stretch capacity 10 inches (25 cm).
— Pull up a section of scrinkle **'1'** and slip scrinkle '2' through it.

Fig. 3
— Twist scrinkle '2' once.
— Put fingers of **right** hand through scrinkle to pull entire ponytail through.
— Twist scrinkle once.

fig.3

Fig. 4
— Put fingers of **_left_** hand through scrinkle to pull entire ponytail through.
— Repeat procedure until all the scrinkle is used.

Fig. 5
— Finished **SCRINKLE PONYTAIL**.

TIPS: Cotton scrinkles do not slide as much as satin or silk.

8. SCRINKLE PONYTAIL (ALTERNATING)

Fig. 1

— Use two scrinkles – each with 8 to 10 inches (20-25 cm) stretch.
— Make ponytail – even with left eyebrow and above left ear.
— When technique is mastered, ponytail may be positioned anywhere desired.
— Place first scrinkle securely around ponytail.
— Wind scrinkle around until it can be wound no more.

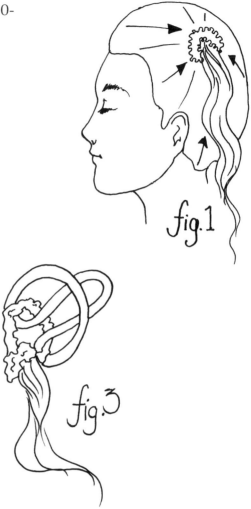

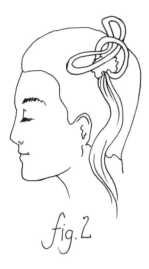

Fig. 2 & Fig. 3

— Pull up the top of scrinkle.
— Put scrinkle '2' through scrinkle '1' and make a slip knot (See **Fig. 3**).

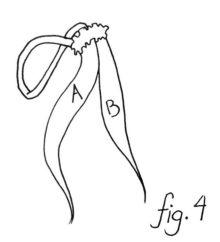

Fig. 4

— Divide ponytail into two strands – 'A' and 'B.'
— Twist scrinkle once.

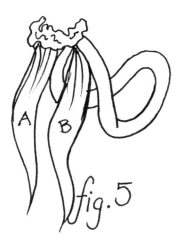

Fig. 5

— Put fingers of left hand through scrinkle and pull 'B' through.
— Twist scrinkle once.
— Put right fingers through scrinkle.

Fig. 6

— Reach over 'B.' Pull 'A' through scrinkle.
— Twist scrinkle once. Put left hand fingers through it.
— Reach over 'A.' Pull 'B' through scrinkle.
— Twist scrinkle once. Put right hand fingers through it.
— Reach over 'B.' Pull 'A' through.
— Repeat procedure until desired ponytail length is reached.
— Join 'A' and 'B.' Pull ponytail through scrinkle.
— Twist scrinkle once.
— Pull ponytail 'AB' through scrinkle once again.

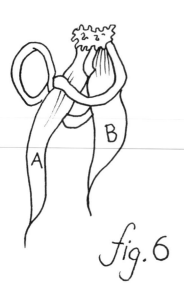

Fig. 7
— Completed **SCRINKLE PONYTAIL (ALTERNATING)**.

9.   REVERSE SCRINKLE

— *Scrinkle must stretch to 9 inches (22.5 cm) in length.*
— *Start style at nape hairline.*

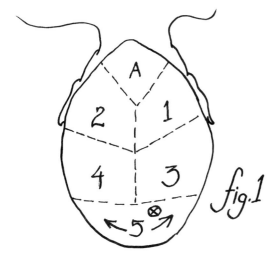

Fig. 1
— Fig. 1 shows various sections and steps used to braid the **REVERSE SCRINKLE**.
— Sections will be large.

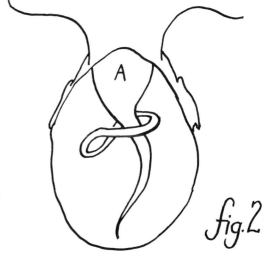

Fig. 2
— Make section 'A.'
— With right hand, put scrinkle around section 'A.'
— Twist scrinkle once. Scrinkle is now around left hand, with only fingers visible.

Fig. 3
— Shaft of 'A' is held by fingers in left hand.
— Take section '1' from right and add it to 'A.'
— Pull 'A' through scrinkle.
— Twist scrinkle once.
— Scrinkle is now around fingers of right hand.

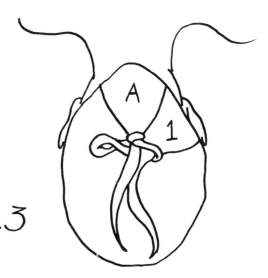

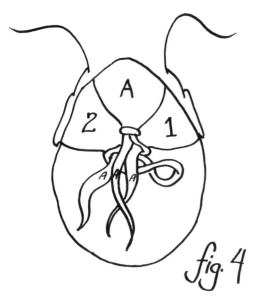

fig. 4

Fig. 4
— Take hair shaft in right hand.
— Feed section '2' into 'A.'
— Pull '2' and 'A' through scrinkle.
— Twist scrinkle once.
— Fingers of left hand are now holding hair shaft 'A.'

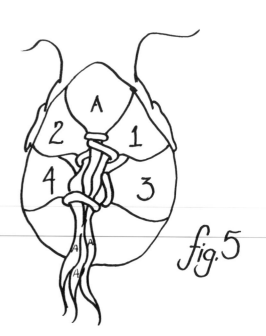

fig. 5

Fig. 5
— Feed section '3' into 'A.'
— Pull '3' and 'A' through scrinkle.
— Twist scrinkle once.
— Fingers of right hand are now holding hair shaft 'A.'
— Feed section '4' into 'A.'
— Pull '4' and 'A' through scrinkle.
— Twist scrinkle once.
— Fingers of left hand are now holding hair shaft 'A.'

Fig. 6
— Notice 'X' to the right of center of head.
— Position hand at 'X.'
— Feed all section '5' into hair shaft 'A.'
— Twist scrinkle once.
— Allow hair shaft to hang in a ponytail.

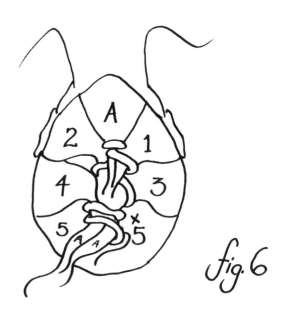

fig. 6

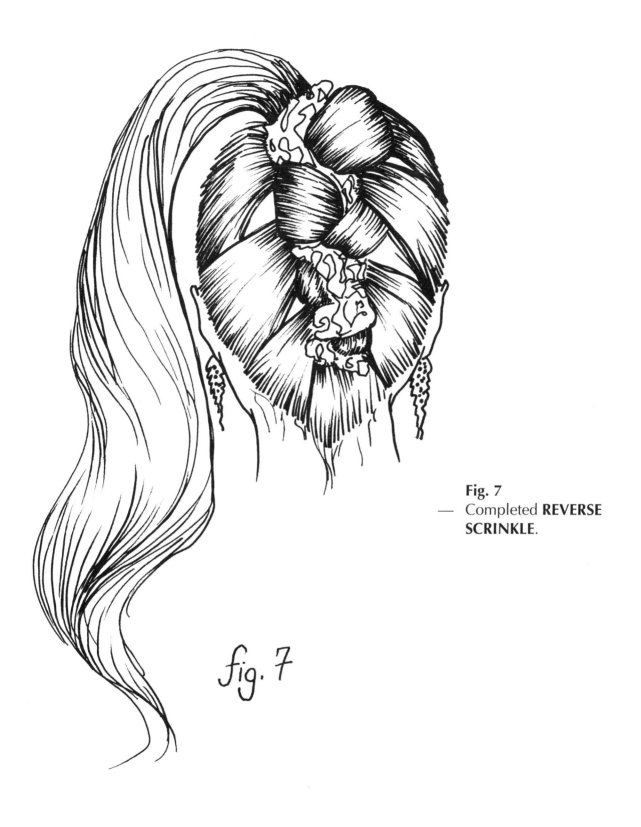

Fig. 7
— Completed **REVERSE SCRINKLE**.

fig. 7

TIPS: Alternate Finish – Tuck ponytail under and secure with bobby pin.

Chapter 7 — Twist Braiding

1. LINDSAY'S TWO SIDED TWIST BRAID

Fig. 1
— Make center part from front hairline to nape.
— On right side of head make triangle section 'A.'
— Divide 'A' into two strands to make top strand #1, and bottom strand #2.
— Bring #2 up over #1 and back down.

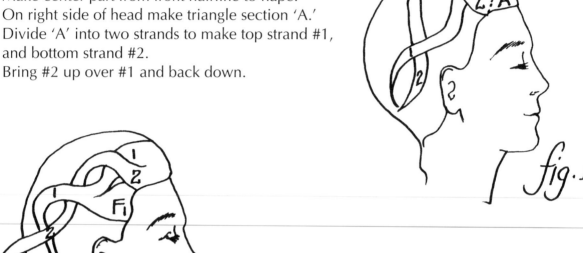

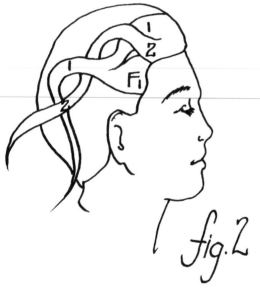

Fig. 2
— Take feeding section 'F-1' from hairline. Feed it into strand #1.
— Bring #1 down.

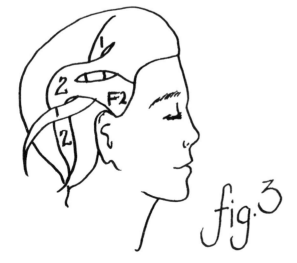

Fig. 3
— Take 'F-2' from hairline. Feed it into strand #2.
— Strand #1 crosses up, over strand #2.
— Strand #2 comes down.
— Repeat procedure to center area.
— Secure braid at nape next to scalp and center part.

Fig. 4

— Left side – make section 'B.'
— Divide 'B' into two strands to make top strand #1 and bottom strand #2.
— #2 goes up and over #1.
— Bring #1 down.

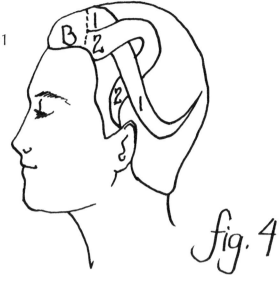

fig. 4

fig. 5

Fig. 5

— Take feeding section 'F-1' from hairline. Feed it into strand #1.
— Strand #2 crosses up and over #1.
— Bring #1 down.
— Repeat procedure until all hair from left hairline is fed into braid.
— Always feed into top section.

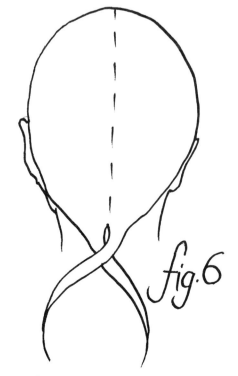

fig. 6

Fig. 6

— Cross right braid over left braid to combine them.
— Secure with elastic.
— Cover elastic with barrette or bow.

Fig. 7
— Completed **LINDSAY'S TWO SIDED TWIST BRAID**.

fig. 7

TIPS: Size of feeding sections will be determined by thickness of the hair.

2. ONE-SIDED TWIST BRAID

Fig. 1
— Comb all hair to right side of head (see arrows).
— Section as shown by dots.
— Divide section into two strands.
— Bottom strand #2 goes over strand #1.

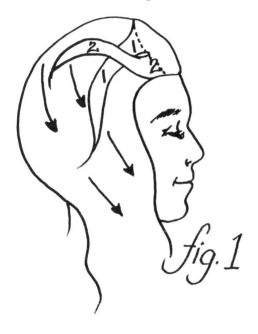

fig. 1

Fig. 2
— Keep all hair hanging over right hairline.
— Take section 'F' – feed it into #2.
— #1 crosses over #2.
— #2 comes down.

fig. 2

Fig. 3
— Take another section 'F' from right.
— Feed 'F' into #1.
— #2 crosses over #1.
— #1 comes down.
— Repeat procedure until all hairline hair, to nape, is fed into braid.
— Secure braid with elastic, at hairline.
— Cover elastic with barretted bow.
— Curl free hanging hair.

fig. 3

Fig. 4
— Completed **ONE-SIDED TWIST BRAID**.

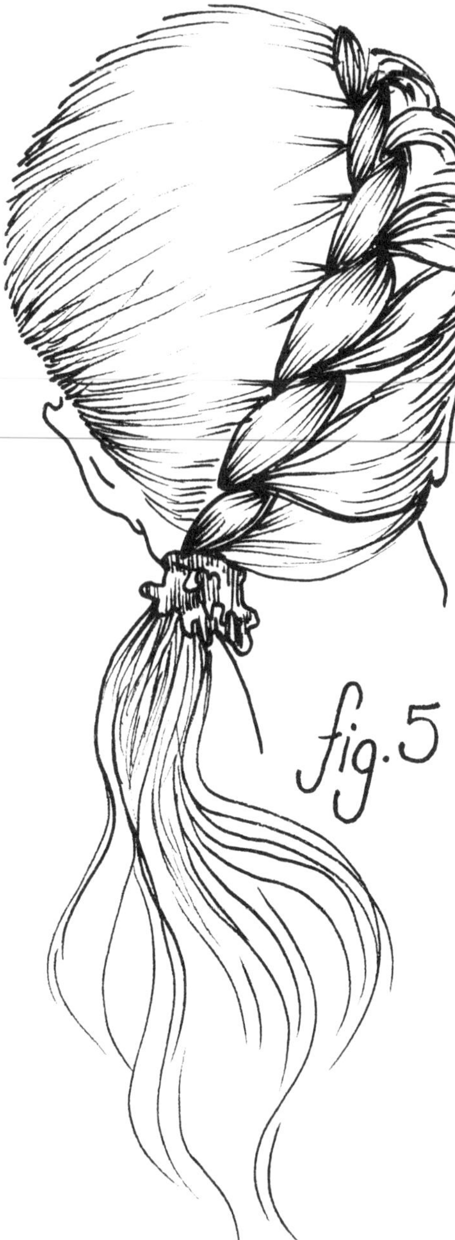

fig. 4

fig. 5

Fig. 5
— **DIAGONAL ONE-SIDED TWIST BRAID**.

3. REVERSE TWIST BRAID

Fig. 1
— Section hair as shown by dots.
— Divide section into two equal strands.
— Comb and smooth all free hair to **your** right.

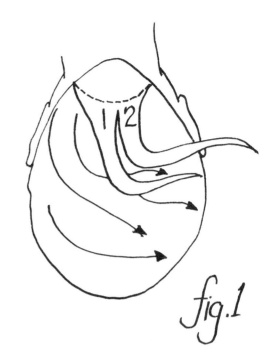

fig.1

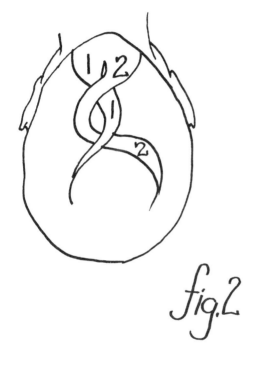

fig.2

Fig. 2
— Cross strand #2 over, then under strand #1.
  (Strand #1 is now on top. Strand #2 is
  bottom strand).

Fig. 3
— Take section 'F' from right side.
— Feed 'F' into strand #1.
— Strand #1 goes under #2.
— Take section 'F' from right side.
— Feed 'F' into strand #2.
— Strand #2 goes under #1.

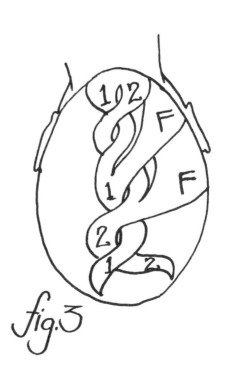

fig.3

Fig. 4
— Repeat last two steps until braid reaches top of head.
— Twist hair shaft to *your* left (c.c.w.).
— Continue twisting hair shaft, holding securely.
— Secure with elastic near end of twisted braid.
— Coil braid in c.c.w. direction.
— Secure coil with hairpins.

fig. 4

Fig. 5
— Completed **REVERSE TWIST BRAID**.

fig. 5

TIPS: C.C.W. – Counter-clockwise.

Chapter 8 — Knot Braiding

1. HORIZONTAL GET KNOTTY

Fig. 1
— Comb the hair straight back.
— Divide the hair into four equal sections, 'A,' 'B,' 'C,' 'D.'

Fig. 2
— Fig. 2 shows how to make a hair knot.
— Practice making the knot before proceeding with the hairstyle.

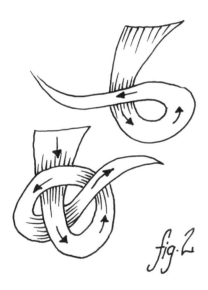

fig.2

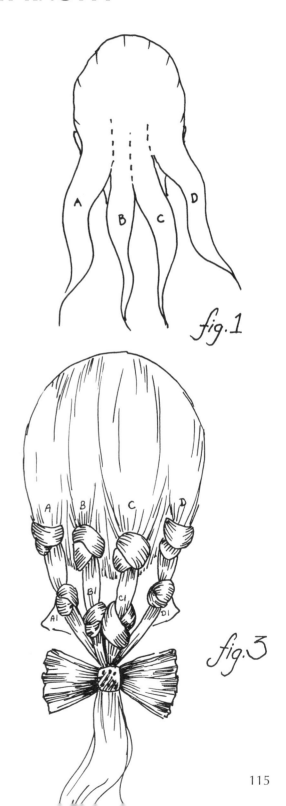

fig.1

fig.3

Fig. 3
— Tie a knot at the top of each strand.
— Keep knots even horizontally.
— Tie a second knot in each of 'A' and 'D' – keeping them even with each other (A1 and D1).
— Slightly lower than 'A1' and 'D1', tie a second knot in each of 'B' and 'C' (B1, C1).
— 2 inches (5 cm) down from last knots – join all 4 strands and secure with an elastic.
— Cover elastic with a bow.

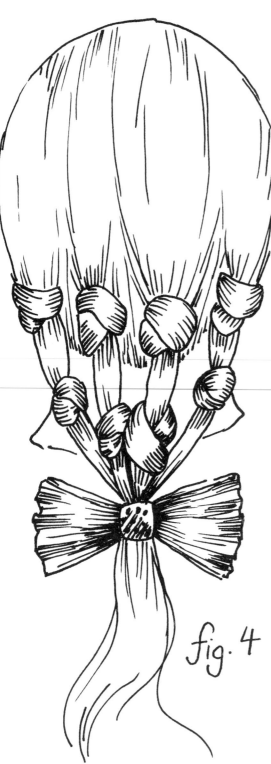

fig. 4

Fig. 4
— Finished **HORIZONTAL GET KNOTTY**.

TIPS: Hair length should be to middle of back for this style.

2. LOW SINGLE TIE KNOT

Fig. 1
— Section head of hair to make section 'A.'

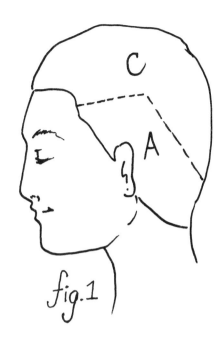

fig. 1

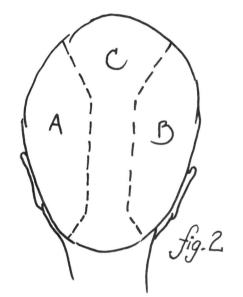

fig. 2

Fig. 2
— Now section hair to make section 'B.'

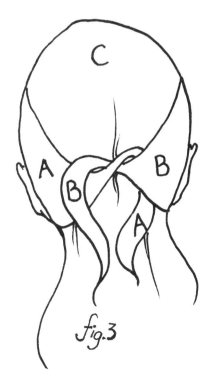

fig. 3

Fig. 3
— With 'A' and 'B' make one tie, as if tying a shoelace.
— 'A' goes *over* 'B,' then *under*.
— 'B' goes *under* 'A,' then *over*.

Fig. 4
— Tie again to form a knot.
— 'A' goes **under** 'B,' then **over**.
— 'B' goes **over** 'A,' then **under**.
— Bring 'A' and 'B' together. Tie tail 'AB' with a scrinkle.

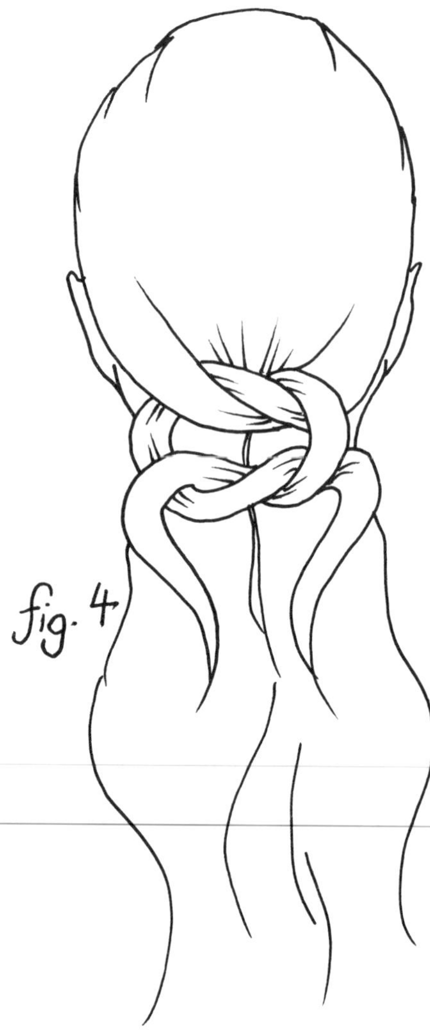

fig. 4

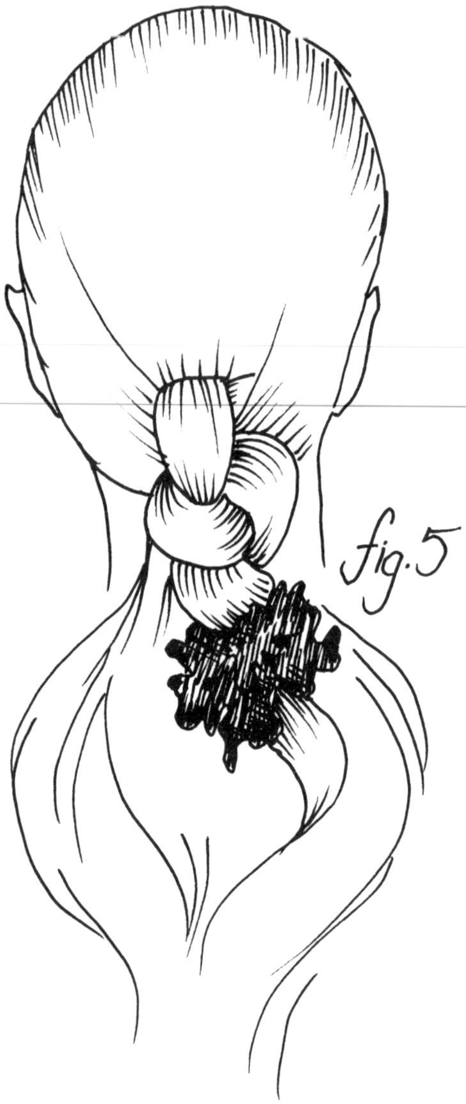

fig. 5

Fig. 5
— Completed **LOW SINGLE TIE KNOT**.

TIPS: Put elastic around tail 'AB.' Place a bow or large barrette over elastic.

3. JENNIFER'S TRIPLE PONYTAIL KNOTS

Fig. 1
— Section hair as shown in Fig. 1.
— Section 'A' on both the left and right sides.
— Sections 'A,' 'B,' 'C,' are the working sections.

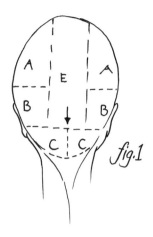

Fig. 2
— Continue to section hair as shown in Fig. 2.

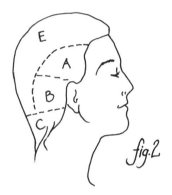

Fig. 3
— Bring the two 'A' sections together at crown and tie in a shoestring knot.
— Hold shaft of hair securely beneath knot.
— Put elastic around shaft, just below knot.

Fig. 4
— Dots indicate where to start next parting. (Begin at hairline behind middle of ear).

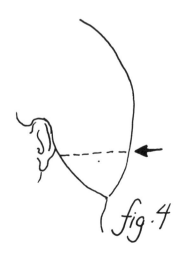

Fig. 5

— Make a straight horizontal part toward center to make section 'B.'
— Part only to the left side of 'E' shaft and stop. 'B' section ends here.
— As 'B' section is taken, move 'E' section a bit to one side (to avoid picking up hair from 'E').
— 'E' section hangs down back of head – not joined into any other sections.
— Join left and right 'B' sections.

fig.5

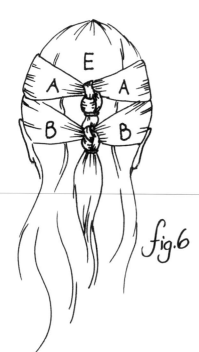

fig.6

Fig. 6.

— Put elastic just below knot.
— Third knot is made from 'C' sections.
— Pull E section to one side. Use remaining hair at hairline to make 'C' sections.

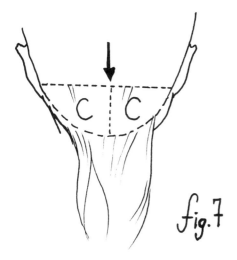

fig.7

Fig. 7

— Arrow indicates center part for 'C' sections.
— Follow same procedure.
— Bring 'C' sections together.
— Tie 'C' sections in a knot and put elastic below knot.
— Spread out rest of free hanging shaft.

Fig. 8
— Completed **JENNIFER'S TRIPLE PONYTAIL KNOT**.

fig. 8

TIPS: Be sure knots are in line with one another. All sections should be snug and secure against head. Elastics are to be tight.

4. DIAGONAL GET KNOTTY QUAD

Fig. 1
— Section hair on right side.
— Make a horizontal part from the temple, and a slightly vertical part from behind the ear.
— This is now section 'A.'

Fig. 2
— Using all of section 'A,' make a knot as shown in Fig. 2.
— Be sure the knot is close to the head with tight tension.

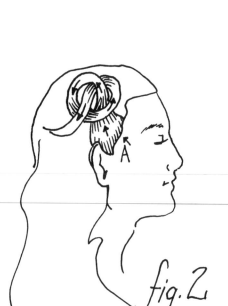

Fig. 3
— Take a large section of hair, 'B,' and feed it into the shaft, after first knot. (Fig. 3)
— Make another knot, same method as Fig. 2.

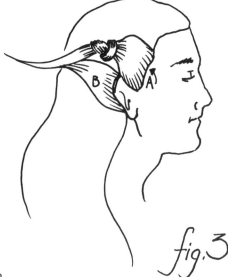

Fig. 4

— Fig. 4 shows positioning of knots.
— First knot should be 2 inches (5 cm) above the ear and in line with the back of ear.
— Second knot should be below crown area.
— Third knot position is slightly lower than second knot.
— Fourth knot may be back of middle of ear, or back of ear lobe (personal preference).
— Secure last knot, at the back, with a bobby pin (keeps it from shifting).
— Remaining hair shaft will hang over left shoulder.

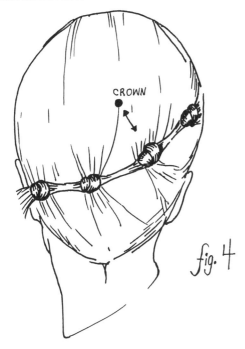

fig. 4

Fig. 5

— Completed **DIAGONAL GET KNOTTY QUAD**.

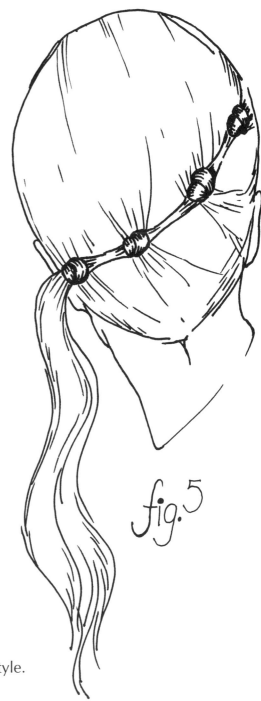

fig. 5

TIPS: Hair length should be to middle of back for this style.

5. TRIPLE TIE KNOT

fig.1

Fig. 1
— Section the hair as in Fig. 1.
— Dotted line shows designated pattern to follow.
— Divide section 'A' into two strands.

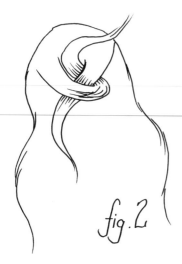

fig.2

Fig. 2
— Tie the two strands together once (Fig. 2).

Fig. 3
— Tie again to make a tie knot (Fig. 3).

fig.3

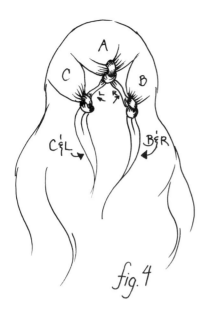

fig. 4

Fig. 4
— Make two new sections 'B' and 'C' as indicated in Fig. 4.
— Feed 'B' into 'R.' Tie in a complete tie knot.
— To make knot lay close and secure against head, take a small strand from hair lying under 'RB' knot. Include it with 'RB' tail and secure with an elastic.
— Repeat procedure with 'C' and 'L.'

Fig. 5
— Completed **TRIPLE TIE KNOT**.

fig. 5

Chapter 9 — Self Braiding

1. VERTICLE INVISIBLE BRAID

Use of basic terms makes the braiding process easier to understand. The terms, and their meaning for Invisible Braiding, follow.

Fist: All four fingers around a strand of hair.
Pinch: Thumb and index fingers holding a strand of hair.
Vise: Middle finger and index finger holding a strand of hair.

No head diagrams are included for this braid, for you will be doing it on yourself. Use the proper hand positions that relate to the instructions. When braiding one's own hair, the hands are always palms down.

fig. 1

Fig. 1
— Start at the center front, taking a small section of hair (Fig. 1).
— Divide section into three strands.
— Left hand will participate first.

Fig. 2
— Left Hand: **Fist** the left outside strand.
— **Pinch** the middle strand.

fig. 2

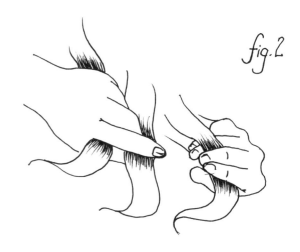

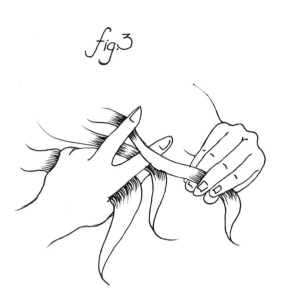

Fig. 3
— Cross **right** outside strand over middle and put in left **vise**.

Fig. 4
— Right Hand: **Fist** what is in **left pinch**.
— **Pinch** what is in left **vise**.

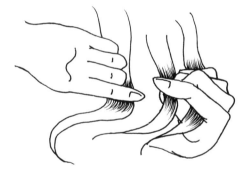

Fig. 5
— Cross **left** outside strand into **right** vise.

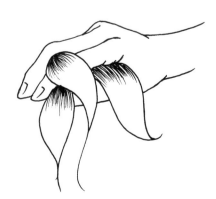

Fig. 6
— Left Hand: ***Fist*** what is in ***right pinch***.
— ***Pinch*** what is in right ***vise***.

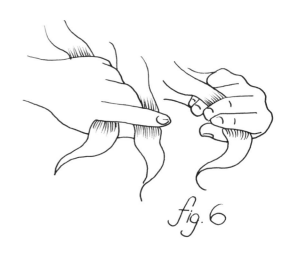

fig. 6

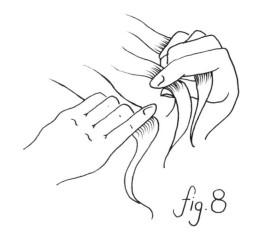

fig. 7

Fig. 7
— Cross ***right*** outside strand into ***left*** vise.
— Pick up section of hair from ***right hairline*** and feed into ***left vise***.

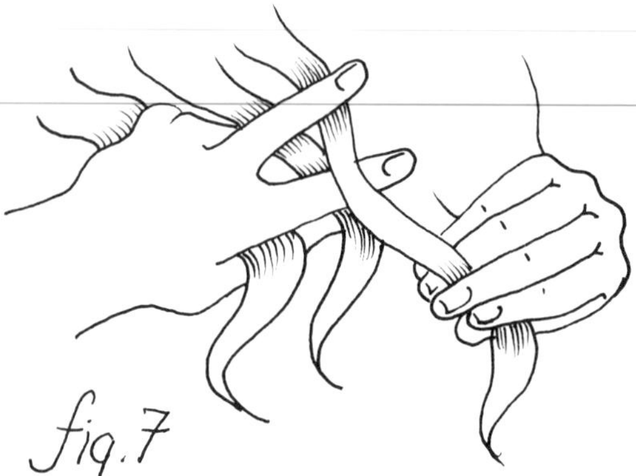

Fig. 8
— Right Hand: Fist what is in ***left pinch***.
— ***Pinch*** what is in left vise.

fig. 8

Fig. 9
— Cross *right* outside strand into *left* vise.
— Pick up a section of hair from *left hairline* and feed it into *right* vise.
— Repeat steps in Figs. 6, 7 and Figs. 8, 9 until you run out of hair to feed in.
— Continue braiding the pigtail until 2 inches (5 cm) before end of hair shaft.
— Tie off pigtail with elastic.

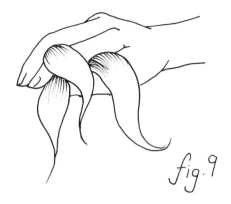

fig. 9

Fig. 10
— Completed **VERTICLE INVISIBLE BRAID**.

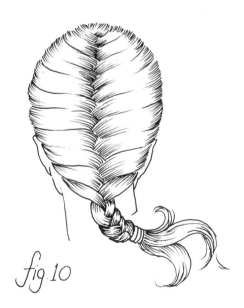

fig. 10

TIPS: Remember the method is: Fist, Pinch, Cross Over Into Vise. With this method you may go diagonally or horizontally on your head. Each direction gives a total new look (style).

You may tuck the pigtail under the braid and wear a bow or barrette at the base of the style.

2.   VERTICLE VISIBLE BRAID

Use of basic terms makes the braiding process easier to understand. The terms, and their meaning for Visible Braiding, follow.

> *Fist:*   *All four fingers around a strand of hair.*
> *Pinch:*   *Thumb and index finger holding a strand of hair.*
> *Vise:*   *Middle finger and index finger holding a strand of hair.*

No head diagrams are included for this braid, for you will be braiding on yourself. Use the proper hand positions that relate to the instructions.

When braiding one's own hair, the hands are always palms down.

fig.1

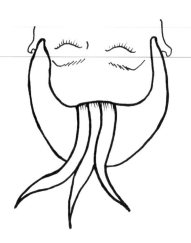

Fig. 1
— Start at the center front, taking a small section of hair.
— Divide section into three strands.
— Right hand will participate first.

fig.2

Fig. 2
— Right Hand: *Fist* right outside strand.
— Put middle strand in right vise.
— *Pinch* left outside strand.

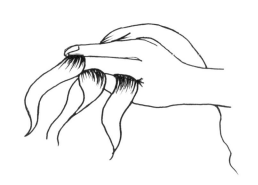

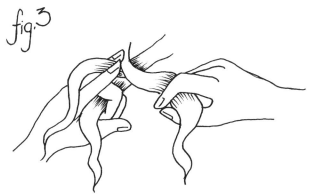

fig. 3

Fig. 3
— Left Hand: *Fist* what is in *right vise*.
— *Vise* what is in *right* pinch.

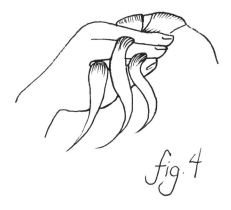

fig. 4

Fig. 4
— *Pinch* what is in *right fist*.

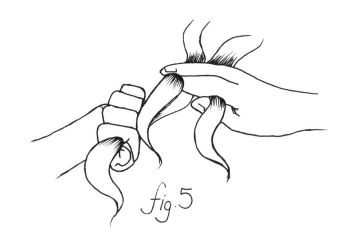

fig. 5

Fig. 5
— Right Hand: Fist what is in *left vise*.
— Vise what is in *left* pinch.

Fig. 6
— Pinch what is in *left* fist.
— Now *feed* section of hair from left hairline into *right pinch*.

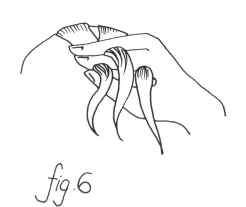

fig. 6

Fig. 7
— Left Hand: Fist what is in **right vise**.
— Vise what is in right pinch.

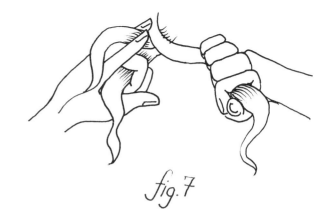

fig. 7

Fig. 8
— **Pinch** what is in **right fist**.
— Now **feed** section of hair from right hairline **into left pinch**.
— Repeat steps in Figs. 5, 6 and Figs. 7, 8 until you run out of hair to feed in.
— Continue braiding the pigtail until 2 inches (5 cm) before the end of hair shaft.
— Tie off pigtail with elastic.

fig. 8

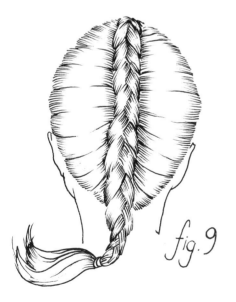

fig. 9

Fig. 9
— Completed **VERTICLE VISIBLE BRAID**.

TIPS: Cover elastic with a scrinkle, ribbon, or small barrette.

With this braiding method you may also have a diagonal or horizontal style.

3.   VERTICAL TWO STRAND BRAID

Use of basic terms makes the braiding process easier to understand. The terms, and their meaning for Two Strand, follow.

> *Fist:*   *All four fingers around a strand of hair.*
> *Pinch:* *Index and thumb holding a strand of hair.*
> *Vise:*   *Middle finger and index finger holding a strand of hair.*

Head diagrams are not shown, for you will be braiding on yourself. Use the proper hand positions that relate to the instructions.

When braiding one's own hair, the hands are palms down.

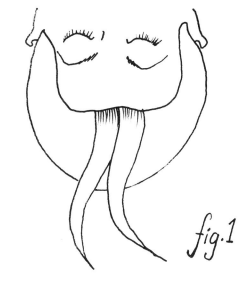

Fig. 1
— Start at center front, taking a small section of hair.
— Divide section into two strands.
— **Left hand** will participate first.

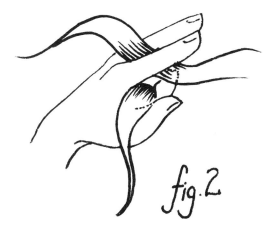

Fig. 2
— Left Hand: **Fist** left strand.
— Strand on right crosses over and into left vise.

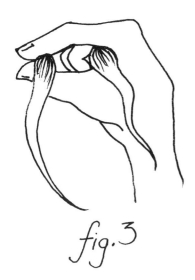

fig. 3

Fig. 3
— Right Hand: **Fist** what is in **left fist**.
— **Pinch** what is in **left vise**.

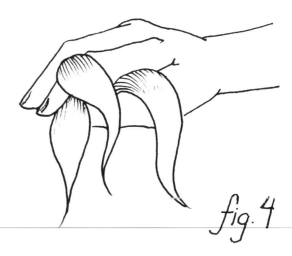

fig. 4

Fig. 4
— **Feed** hair from **left** hairline into **right** vise.

Fig. 5
— Left Hand: **Fist** what is in **right pinch**.
— Now put **right** vise with **right** fist (making one strand).
— Pinch right fist with left pinch.

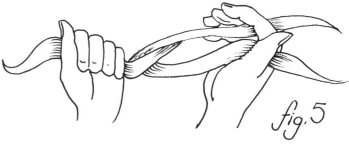

fig. 5

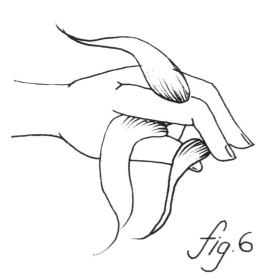

fig. 6

Fig. 6
— **Feed** hair from **right** hairline into **left** vise.

Fig. 7
— Right Hand: *Fist* what is in *left pinch*.
— Put *left* vise with *left* fist (making one strand).
— Pinch left fist with *right pinch*.

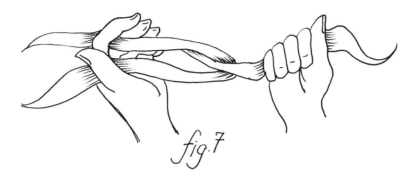

Fig. 8
— *Feed* hair from *left* hairline into *right* vise.
— Repeat this procedure, (Fig. 5, 6 and Fig. 7, 8), until all skull hair is braided.

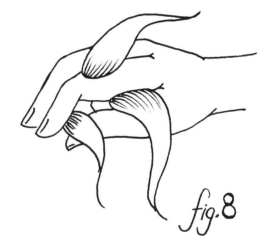

Fig. 9
— Continue to braid tail.
— Last *hand position*, (assume it is left hand).

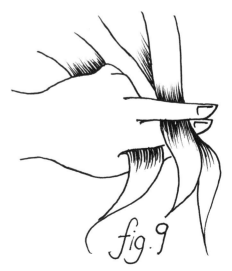

Fig. 10-1
— Take 1/8 inch (0.3 cm) of right outer strand (your pinch).

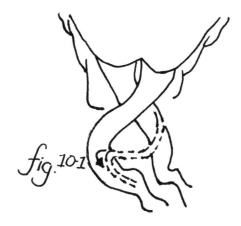

fig. 10-1

Fig. 10-2
— Feed into left vise.

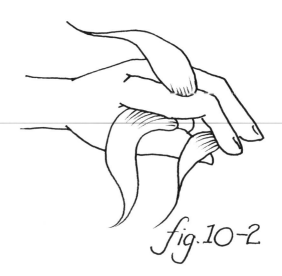

fig. 10-2

Fig. 11
— Right Hand: Fist what is in left pinch.
— Put *left* vise with *left* fist (making one strand).
— Pinch *left* fist with *right pinch*.

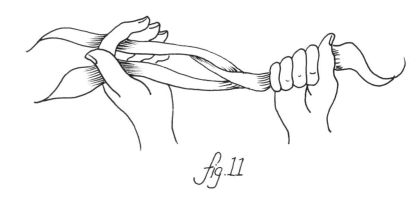

fig. 11

Fig. 12-1

— Take 1/8 inch (0.3 cm) of left outer strand (your pinch).

fig. 12-1

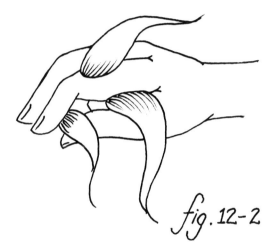

fig. 12-2

Fig. 12-2

— Feed into *right* vise.

Fig. 13

— Left Hand: Fist what is in right pinch.
— Put right vise with right fist (making one strand).
— Pinch *right* fist with *left pinch*.
— Repeat procedure until 2 inches (5 cm) from end of tail shaft.
— Tie pigtail with elastic.

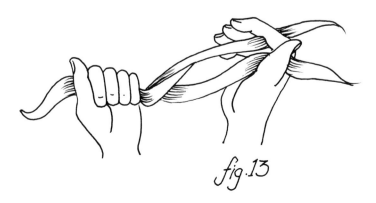

fig. 13

Fig. 14
— Completed **VERTICLE TWO STRAND BRAID**.

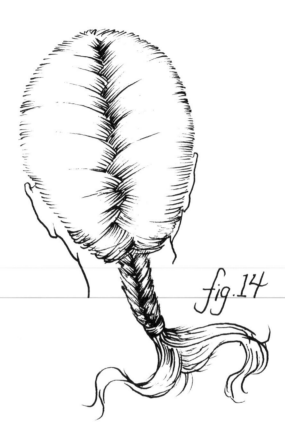

fig.14

TIPS: For evening wear tuck only the very end of pigtail under the braid, leaving majority of the tail visible. Put a bow or an attractive barrette at the base of the skull(pigtail being visible below accessory).

For sports wear let the pigtail hang free and cover elastic with a tailored accessory.

Please send:

☐   Copies of BRAIDS & MORE

☐   Copies of BRAIDS & STYLES FOR LONG HAIR

           $19.95 per copy

_____ GST (7% of Book Total Balance for CANADA ONLY)

_____ $3.00 for POSTAGE & HANDLING IN CANADA

_____ $4.00 for POSTAGE & HANDLING IN U.S.A.

MAIL ALL ORDERS TO: **BRAIDS & STYLES FOR LONG HAIR**
                                    P.O. Box 73054
                                    #206, 2525 Woodview Drive S.W.
                                    Calgary, AB
                                    Canada T2W 6E4

CHEQUES AND MONEY ORDERS MADE PAYABLE TO, "BRAIDS & STYLES FOR LONG HAIR".

Name _____

Address _____

City _____ Province of State _____

Country _____ Postal Code or Zip Code _____

THANK YOU!

Please send:

☐   Copies of BRAIDS & MORE

☐   Copies of BRAIDS & STYLES FOR LONG HAIR

           $19.95 per copy

_____ GST (7% of Book Total Balance for CANADA ONLY)

_____ $3.00 for POSTAGE & HANDLING IN CANADA

_____ $4.00 for POSTAGE & HANDLING IN U.S.A.

MAIL ALL ORDERS TO: **BRAIDS & STYLES FOR LONG HAIR**
                                    P.O. Box 73054
                                    #206, 2525 Woodview Drive S.W.
                                    Calgary, AB
                                    Canada T2W 6E4

CHEQUES AND MONEY ORDERS MADE PAYABLE TO, "BRAIDS & STYLES FOR LONG HAIR".

Name _____

Address _____

City _____ Province of State _____

Country _____ Postal Code or Zip Code _____

THANK YOU!